Dedicated to all those players who have suffered severe injury whilst playing Rugby League. All profits from the sale of this book will, hopefully, alleviate much of that suffering.

League Tales

By
Ray French

RAY FRENCH

Ray French began his rugby league career in 1961, having already gained four Union caps for England. Over the next ten years at St. Helens and Widnes he won both the Challenge Cup and the Championship and joined Great Britain for the World Cup tour of 1968, thus becoming one of the few to have gained international honours in both codes of rugby.

Rugby League correspondent for the Today newspaper for eight years and writer for the "Rugby Leaguer" newspaper for the past twenty three years, he is currently a commentator on the sport for BBC TV and Radio.

The author of several books, including 'The Match of My Life', 'My Kind of Rugby' and 'Ray French's 100 Great Rugby League Players' he retired from teaching English and coaching rugby at Cowley School in St Helens in September 1994.

League Tales

By
Ray French

Published by Ray French

Printed by Colourplan of St.Helens

LEAGUE TALES

Published by Ray French.
Copyright © Ray French 2000

All illustrations were kindly produced by
Mick Hollinworth.

Book design by Dominic McCormack.

This book was typeset in New Baskerville.

ISBN: 0-9539003-0-4

Printed in Great Britain by
Colourplan Design & Print
St.Helens, Merseyside,
England.

Introduction

A fascination for medieval literature and a passion for rugby were the underlying factors which caused me to attempt a parody of Geoffrey Chaucer's 'Canterbury Tales'. The humour, hypocrisy, farce and above all, the humanity displayed in his characters, are timeless. Such characteristics are also to the fore in my world of Rugby League and, as with Chaucer's tales, the tellers of the stories have their roots in the truth. All of the characters portrayed in 'League Tales' are real figures whom I have encountered during my playing career.

Some will be instantly recognisable to my contempories as individual portraits; some are a composite edition of many people I have met in a fifty year association with the code. All of the incidents, serious or comical, and however incredulous, are true and re-told in the hope that, as Chaucer presented a vivid understanding of his fourteenth century world by basing his fiction upon facts, I, in more humble fashion, can present a picture of the smaller, humorous world of Rugby League during my own playing days in the Sixties and Seventies.

Ray French

Preface

If Geoffrey Chaucer, fourteenth century Clerk of Works,
ambassador, forester, controller of Customs, and the father of
English verse, lived in the twentieth century his talents would
have qualified him for yet another occupation - rugby league club
secretary. Such was his insight into character and his amused
tolerance of mankind that he had little trouble in recounting
sympathetically the adventures of his fellow pilgrims when he set
out from the Tabard Inn at Southwark to visit the tomb of
Thomas 'A' Beckett in Canterbury.

With a like compassion for the weaknesses of his colleagues and
with a similar fondness for a humorous story his modern
counterpart, Dick Armstrong, City Rugby League club secretary,
recounts his own tales. Dick's pilgrims, like Chaucer's, embrace a
cross section of life, some good, some bad, but, unlike their
predecessors of the 1400s his pilgrimage takes them on the path
to the shrine of all rugby league followers at Wembley Stadium.
They are "Up For'T Cup" and on a journey dear to the world of
rugby league. And, as with Geoffrey Chaucer's original pilgrims,
Dick Armstrong's stories portray a harsh but lively and amusing
world both on and beyond the highway.

City R.L.F.C.

Abbey Road,
Manchester,
Lancashire.

Colours	Red and White Stripes, White Shorts
Formed	1893
Chairman	H Baker
Directors	B Higson, S Cartwright, C Cartwright, C Taylor, C Chapman, T Partridge
Secretary	R Armstrong
Coach	L Topping
Captain	S Pearson
Ground Capacity	32,000
Record Attendance	31,500 v Wigan. 3rd February 1953
Record Victory	72 pts - 6 pts v Batley 19th April 1965
Record Defeat	3 pts - 57 pts v Leeds 6th March 1921
Highest Points Scorer	D Thompson 26 pts v York 1965
Highest Try Scorer	A Proudlove 53 tries 1956/7
Highest Goal Scorer	D Thompson 193 goals 1964/5
Championship Winners	1930/31, 1933/34, 1956/57, 1959/60, 1964/65, 1965/66
Challenge Cup	1931, 1936, 1964, 1971
Lancashire Cup	1925, 1930, 1933, 1962, 1970
Lancashire League	1925, 1930, 1933, 1965

When May, with its cheering breezes and welcome sun, restores the
spectators to shirt sleeves, removes the protective straw from around the
edges of the pitch, and encourages the grass to clothe the bare patches of
winter, then families' thoughts turn towards the Rugby League Challenge
Cup Final. From Millom and Workington, from Wigan and Golborne,
from Heckmondwike and Huddersfield they make their way, once a year,
decked out in coloured hats, coloured scarves, and even more garishly
coloured suits and dresses to the shrine of all rugby league followers -
Wembley Stadium. Once there, they jostle for attention with the
programme sellers, the raucous Hot Dog vendors, the tight lipped ticket
touts, the rosy cheeked rosette makers, and the swarthy ice cream
merchants. "A wonderful family occasion" is tapped out on the typewriters
of misty eyed journalists perched high in the lofts of the grandstand whilst
television cameras, perched even higher, scan around for the laughing
policeman as he takes a stick of mint humbug (in City colours of course)
from a chubby, double chinned, grandmother.
But think of me, Dick Armstrong, City club secretary, nine years behind
the desk, and a wife, three kids, forty five players, one tea girl, two skip
men, and twelve Directors to support. Few do, that first Saturday in May
and even less on this Monday morning in June, but, without our efforts
during the season, there would be no pilgrimage down the M1. Well, so I
like to think, though at times I wonder why I ever let Harold Baker talk
me into becoming club secretary. He didn't so much talk me into the job
as drink me into it. It's surprising what a grown man will agree to when
six double whiskies in the Black Bull have conjured up visions of himself
sitting on the surround wall as an eight year old roaring his favourites on.
"Put something back in the club," said Harry, the Chairman, "You'll

enjoy the involvement!"
I do mostly, but that telephone rules your life. Where is it? Under those
Wembley programmes. Must send them off to our overseas supporters.
Somebody always gets this cord wrapped around the desk calendar.
"Hello. Oh, hello Mr. Hardman, hope everything went well for you.
You've had a good response to the jersey advertising. Yes, the black
lettering did show up well. Especially across Mac's chest when he came
down from the Royal Box. Yes, the TV did go to twenty four countries.
We will certainly give you first option next season on the sponsorship Mr.
Hardman. Yes it has been good for both of us."
I must put that phone on top of the filing cabinet then I don't get tangled
up again. Yes, it's been a good year for both of us. Mr. Hardman, your
fifty thousand pounds was good for City. I don't know how two million
Australian viewers will be attracted to 'Hardman's Central Heating' but
you know best Mr. Hardman. I mustn't grumble though. There's never a
dull moment in this office - Directors arguing, players moaning, ground
staff upset - and me as the referee in the middle. Perhaps that's the secret
of a successful club. But why they can't work harmoniously throughout
the season I'll never know. With all that bother in February between
'Arry, Stan Pearson and Mr. Higson it's a mystery to me how we ever beat
Hunslet in the second round of the cup....

"Before The Board"

"Turn that radio off. And no sugar!" The shout rang through the deserted changing room, along the stone corridor, and up the tea room stairs where it was soon acted upon by a small poker faced lad. It was 'owd 'Arry giving his orders again as he had done at the D day landings when he went over the top. 'Arry, his wellington boots padding about in discarded plasters and with his braces over his grey pullover, tipped back the inevitable flat cap and leaned on his stiff wire brush. A strong scent of Winter Green oils, vaseline, and sweat filled his nostrils on that cold wintry Sunday morning as he surveyed the scene - large plasters, small plasters, dirty plasters, torn plasters and still more plasters littered the floor as if fighting for space among the cold Shandy bottles, shin pads, and wet bedraggled jerseys. The mud and blood of the previous days combat stained the floor where only yesterday 'Arry had placed the crisp and cleanly laundered red and white strip of the locals. The boots, once neatly polished and set in line, lay as they had been tugged off under the benches, waiting to be rubbed and scrubbed again for his master's feet which had sidestepped their way to glory and winning pay for their owner against Hunslet.

"They make more muck than a Shire horse," thought 'Arry as he bent and scraped beneath the benches. Gold! He spied a piece of gold - or to be more precise, soap.

"Waste," he shrieked. The piece was all of one inch in size but such was 'Arry's preoccupation with soap it was rumoured among the players that he had saved the club over five hundred pounds in soap bills last year. Many players imagined 'Arry working deep into the night to patent 'Arry's Original Floating Soap, guaranteed not to go down the drains. Lose your soap and he would put a black mark against your name - no more Uncle Joe's Mint Balls after training. New bootlaces would disappear from a player's boots overnight. Yes, 'Arry's curse would suddenly descend. The soap was placed in the little wooden box beneath the team mirror, to be melted along with the other scraps, ultimately to be remoulded with loving care. The floor was swept, the tables scrubbed, empty bottles were retrieved, and a pair of cracked false teeth were placed in the red cup on the window sill, ready to be claimed by Mac, the punch drunk prop who trained for rugby twice a week and for married women and Newcastle Brown Ale on the other five nights.

"Tea up," squeaked little Sid and 'Arry retired with his mug to the tea room where, stirring the contents of the cup with a ball lacer of ancient origin, he sat down on the top of the stove, his feet dangling, and gently warmed his bottom at a regulation Mark 5.

"Good win," said Sid, for whom City could do no wrong and who lulled himself to sleep every evening to the tune of Abide With Me, prior to him entering the arena in his imaginary Wembley.

"Rubbish!" snapped 'Arry, who was a realist and who still had his own dreams of bygone days when "Coates, Horsforth and Scott," the finest back three ever to put boots on, roamed the fields outside sending shivers down the backs of visiting scrum halves.

"We should have scored forty, they don't make players like they used to. Too soft, all this free milk at school and Halibut Oil capsules. I wouldn't pay 'em in washers," insisted 'Arry.

"You'll be in trouble with Mr. Higson for shutting him out of here, you know," replied little Sid who loved to see 'Arry in conflict with the directors.

"Mr. Higson will do nowt. He knows where his bread's buttered. I can't see him cleaning this little lot out for £25 quid a week. He

wouldn't dirty his coat in here if he could help it. He only comes
to spy on the staff."

It had certainly been a torrid affair at half time as the Vice
Chairman had tried to storm 'Arry's skip room but the gates of
Rome had held fast with only the loss of a door knob.

"We'll end up at the bottom of the league, never mind win the
cup with a display like that." Thus had spoken Mr. Benjamin
Higson, master painter and decorator, owner of the town's largest
construction company, and self styled expert on the art of Rugby
League Football. He had bought his way onto the board in the
mid sixties and had soon managed to secure the painting and
maintenance contract for the whole ground.

"I'll do it all at cost price," had been the cry. Self centred and
smug, he looked upon the players as his personal property.

"They're bloody rubbish, Taylor's making a fool of you, get up
and knock him down. What are you forwards doing? Smith,
Todd, Harrison, get some bloody tackling done and cut out all
that blind side running. Remember the winning bonus you're
on. Earn it!"

The coach listened, tight lipped and ever aware that Mr Benjamin
Higson had a strong vote over his contract while the players,
smarting under the lash of his tongue, squirmed at their inability
and ineffectiveness to respond to his lashings. This was an insult,
an affront to men who, with heads hanging low, knew their game
and who looked upon criticism from a Higson with contempt.

"Look at the bloody state of you. Todd, have you no tie ups? A
smart team off the field is a smart team on the field. You're a
bloody shower." His cliches trotted out as often as the donkeys on
Blackpool Beach.

"You must have pride in yourself and the club. We have an image
to keep up with the public." Everyone knew his image - two

nights per week in the Conservative Club at nine o'clock on the
No 1 Snooker table, an approachable director, one who cares for
the fans...the bullshitter supreme!

"'Arry, open up in there and get some tie ups in here quickly.
Hurry up."

Silence. The coach considered whether to give his half time talk
but felt the presence of Dame fortune hanging over him and
decided to practise restraint.

"'Arry, open up this door and let's have some tie ups in here to
smarten this bloody lot up," he shouted as he tugged at the skip
room door. Silence. A sea of faces, a black, dirty, grimy sea
looked up and centred on the red sea of Mr. Benjamin Higson.
With his composure cracking, he tugged in frantic fashion at the
door and uttered a hoarse cry of "'Arry, tie ups."

"We're shut," came back the reply and the team burst into
nervous laughter when the door knob flew into the air and some
mysterious force caused Mr. Higson to deposit the backside of his
suede coat in the vaseline tin.

"He'll be back after dinner," a brave soul who was near
retirement, volunteered from the back. Higson by now was
purple, his neck bulging over his fur collar, as he extricated
himself from the vaseline tin.

"This is the last bloody straw, you, you're....." He sensed the
animosity all around the dressing room, the situation was
hopeless. He felt unclean with no bell to ring and, making a
rapid exit, he delivered a last retort, "Call yourself a bloody coach,
get some talking done, earn your bloody money and get Hunslet
beaten. You're on television, don't forget."

The players now experienced relief, a warmth invaded the
dressing room, they had indeed been motivated. Hunslet would
be beaten. They would surely see to that.

"Some mysterious force caused Mr. Higson to deposit the backside of his suede coat in the vaseline tin"

"There'll be trouble from him," said 'Arry, now only simmering his bottom on regulation Mark 3. Meanwhile Sid sipped his tea and studied the latest case in the News of the World. "All talk," suggested 'Arry. Sid stretched out on the physiotherapist's table enthralled at the prospects of "the drunken vicar on the last train to Paddington" and all that the headline could conjure up in his mind. 'Arry's feet and bottom were warm now. The heater could be turned off. There was little left to do. The dressing room had been cleaned, the bulging skip bags containing the jerseys and much of the playing surface stood silently awaiting the delicate hands of Alice the washerwoman on Monday.

"Come on Sid, pick up that piece of soap from under the lamp. Waste, that's what it is, waste." Sid bent down to pick up the lost gold, so engrossed and obviously at a critical point in the drunken vicar's exploits that he hit his head on the cupboard door, thus releasing a cascade of white rolls of bandage and assorted jock-straps on to his head.

"Bloody hell, never be fit for Saturday now," thought Sid as he lapsed back into his daydream world. "Still I could be ready for the cup though." 'Arry grinned as Sid grappled with the jock-straps, seemingly alive and intent on strangling him.

"Make sure you put Mac's back, Sid, we can't get any bigger size!" quipped 'Arry.

The dressing room was cold and deserted, empty of its passion, a lonely place on a windswept Sunday when players were still only turning over in their beds and beginning to feel their bruises from the previous day. 'Arry locked the outer door, placed the key behind the loose brick in the wall, tried the door with a tug, and prepared to trudge homeward across the pitch.

"Early today, Sid," he remarked as he thrust a mint ball into his mouth and placed one in Sid's outstretched hand. The wind moaned around the stands, empty of their crowds accustomed to venting their pleasure or displeasure at the local favourites. The red and blue paint gleamed down from the terraces, now blank save for odd piles of windswept paper cartons and programmes, swirling at the foot of the crush barriers.

"Yes, at four pounds fifty per can of Gloss and two pounds for Undercoat, he's made a few bob has our Mr. Higson," thought 'Arry. "Do you remember when Jackson scored in that corner, beat Sam Taylor on his outside, stepped inside Jenkins, and placed it under the sticks? Could have had his tea on the try line. So fast. What a player, eh, Sid."

"Eh," echoed Sid, who by now was giving his full concentration to the drunken vicar.

"Oh you wouldn't know, Sid. You weren't born then."

"Thank God," muttered Sid, lost in a confused orgy of the drunken vicar scoring the last minute try at Wembley while Sid fought off a bevy of scantily clad young girls on the steps of the Royal Box. 'Arry closed the gate behind him, tugged at his cap, set it well down over his forehead against the wind and said, "Higson's no chance, he wants to stick to his painting. Monday's Board meeting could be interesting though. Having to deal with Stan Pearson and myself, there could be some fun for Higson and company."

It had been an auspicious season for Stan, having been selected for Great Britain versus France on two occasions and in both games having played the game of his life. His financial value had rocketed from the five hundred pounds he had received on his sixteenth birthday to many thousands of pounds on the transfer market. He was famous now, not only in Fern Crescent where his kids would welcome his every step up the road but in the whole of the rugged North where man gains respect not only for his

education or politics but for his ability to sidestep off both feet.
Stan Pearson too envisaged fun as, on the Monday evening, clad
in his overalls, he made his way to the club, carefully avoiding the
glare of the training lights under which the rest of the team were
now in full throttle. He slid quietly towards the door at the rear
of the clubhouse. Peering inside and eventually clearing a way
through the steam of the communal bath, now being prepared
for the evening, he sighted 'Arry laying out the towels and soap
for the expected rush of players at about nine o'clock.
"Has the meeting started, 'Arry?"
"Aye," replied 'Arry, without looking up from his task, "they've
been at it for over an hour. They should have picked the full
back now. They're waiting for you, supposed to be sacking me
tonight if Higson gets his way." He grinned and added, "Mind
how you go."
The Board had indeed been at it for over an hour, all seven of
them, in the regular weekly meeting at which all of the club's affairs
came under the careful scrutiny of the local dignitaries of the town.
At the centre of the said scrutineers, sat firmly behind the walnut
table, was the bulky shape of Harold Baker. From head to toe in
his hand cut suit he was a figure of respectability, surely "one on
whom assurance sits like a silk hat on a Bradford millionaire."
He had made his money out of scrap and, during the boom after
the war years, had bought his way onto the Board, whose
operations he had dominated for the last ten years, at least until
the late arrival of Mr. Benjamin Higson. At the side of Harold
Baker's stubby right hand, which perpetually flicked ash from an
ever lit cigarette into a glass ash tray, souvenir of the Queen's
Coronation, sat the brothers Cartwright of Cartwright and
Cartwright, Solicitors. Both now in their early sixties, the
brothers, Sam and Charles, ran one of the longest established and

most successful legal practices in the town and, from early childhood, had been league devotees. Both tended to stand aside from the cut and thrust of the meetings but both, possibly through their strong legal background, invariably gave their backing to the Chairman in times of dispute. "You must have order in a meeting," was Sam's favourite remark whenever he raised his arm to many a Baker inspired proposition. Charles, in particular, viewed Colin Taylor's presence on the board as being that of a mere upstart - "at thirty six years of age, not mature enough to look after the affairs of a club like City."

Both though had been saddened at the recent departure from the Board of Taylor's father through an unfortunate heart attack at the age of seventy six, his shares having passed on to his son. "Young Taylor" was viewed with some concern too by Higson, the Vice-Chairman, who was not yet sure where Taylor's loyalties would lie when he cracked the whip. Nor did he approve of his familiarity with the players in the after match drinking on the way home from a match or his over fraternising at the restaurant tables. "Never be a players' man," Higson was often heard to comment to his disciples on the Board, Partridge and 'Con' Chapman. Often adding, "Taylor needs watching, thinks he's a bloody Redcoat at Butlins the way he fusses after the players."

His disciples were indeed on the Board to listen to and spread the word of Mr. Benjamin Higson for both 'Con' and Ted were co-directors of Higson's Painting, Decorating and Construction Company and, as such, merely nodded their assent to whatever came from Benjamin's mouth. 'Con' however, a lean figure with a slight stoop of the shoulders and a liking for black pin stripe suits, was a figure of some mirth to many on the Board for the way in which he took an independent line. Often when the whisky was flowing in his glass he would take the opposite argument to

Benjamin, poking his finger in the air, as he stressed his point. However, after four whiskies, usually poured by Higson, he would always vote with him at the end of a debate, forgetting whatever arguments he had raised earlier.

With seven providing for a quorum, they had moved through the question of the installation of new turnstiles at the Abbey Road end of the ground and had successfully concluded their discussion of the sponsorship of the playing strip by a local company when, amid a short pause, during which time Higson was playing the role of Barman at the Drinks Cabinet, a knock was heard at the door. Behind the knock stood Stan Pearson, acclaimed as his country's finest stand off, but now standing uneasily in his oil stained overalls awaiting his entrance.

"Come in," Higson called from alongside the Drinks Cabinet. "Oh, Hello Stan, this is a pleasure, now what can we do for you? A couple of tickets for the cup match for Doreen and her mother?" said Harold Baker. Higson continued to replenish the directors' drinks and, having placed them on the table, remained standing, leaning casually at the side of the cabinet seemingly uninterested in the ensuing interview. But, in allowing Harold Baker to conduct it he strained both ears and watched Stan Pearson with a keen interest.

"Er, no, Mr Baker, no. It's a personal matter."

"Cigarette, Stan?"

"No thanks Mr Baker, you know I don't smoke. I need a thousand pounds, Mr Baker, to put an extension on the house for Doreen."

"But Stan," replied Mr Baker, flicking his ash into the glass tray and with his face as composed as a defeated politician's in a Bye Election, "you just can't come in here and ask for money. It's illegal. If the league found out where would we be?"

"Don't be daft, Mr Baker, everybody's had a backhander here at

City. If you are a star the money's there, if you're not, the money's not. You keep telling me I'm the star. What now?"

"I agree with Mr Baker, Stan," chipped in Sam Cartwright, "a club has to be run on a legal basis or there would be chaos. We have contracts now."

"The Board would like to help if it could but we are a bit short of money at the moment Stan," wailed Mr. Baker. "It's a bad time at the moment. We are looking for a good run in the cup. And we have just paid £15,000 for Bates the new Union signing who we hope will boost the crowds and help us to put more winning money in all your pockets."

"I suppose I don't put any on the gate then, except Doreen and her mother," said Stan, now warming to the discussion.

"We all know your value to the club but remember that if you cause trouble now before the cup tie you will let the whole team down. You're playing for City now Stan," urged 'Con' Chapman.

"I'm playing for Doreen, myself and them two kids, 'Con'. When I signed on, Mr. Baker, and you pushed a cheque for five hundred pounds into my hand, you said 'you're playing for money now my lad, look after it and earn as much as you can.' Believe me, I'm doing just that. I need that thousand pounds."

"Well Stan, you should know that City won't put up with an awkward customer. We can be awkward too if we are pushed. We can stop your rugby and your pay easy enough," insisted Mr. Baker.

"We play that Cup tie, Mr. Baker, and you need a stand off to cope with Benson. If we lose then there'll be hell on this town and you know it. Don't put it in the press that I've got a pulled muscle because I'll get on to Phil King in the Sunday People. He'll let the fans know in his column."

"Think it over, Stan," replied Harold Baker, "don't be rash and do something you might regret. We will help you out if we can but there's no money at the moment. We will defer selection until Thursday to see how you feel then."

"I'll feel the same as I do now," snapped Stan, "there's no way I'll be here at the weekend."

Colin Taylor shuffled uneasily in his seat, smiled at Stan and turned to Harold Baker, "Is there nothing we can do for Stan to help him at the moment, perhaps a loan? He's been a tremendous servant to the club and he would certainly be missed by the lads in this cup-tie." Harold Baker's eyes swivelled onto Taylor and only the tossing in of a grenade could have brought about a similar reaction from the others seated at the table as the hearing of Taylor's plea for Stan. Only the sound of a glass being laid on the top of the cocktail cabinet indicated any reaction from Mr Benjamin Higson but anyone who had observed the sudden raising of his eyebrows in exasperation at Taylor's remark would have known that now was the time at which he felt it necessary to intervene.

"Mr. Baker's right, you know Pearson."

Taylor was silenced. Another grenade had been thrown and Harold Baker stopped momentarily from lighting another cigarette from the remains of the one already in his mouth. The finality of the support from Higson for Baker's own attitude was welcome but only the necessity of maintaining a firm hold on his cigarette between his lips stopped him from revealing his initial reaction of shock at the suddenness of the supporting intrusion.

"There's not that kind of money around at the moment. The club's interests must always come before the individual. Don't forget we have the public to think of in these matters. Can't you see this?"

Before Stan could 'see this' and before he could open his mouth Higson delivered a crushing blow to the thoughts in his head with,

"Haven't we a job for a welder with the Construction Company at the moment 'Con'? I believe it's a five and a half days week for twenty pounds. Not bad wages that on top of winning bonuses."
'Con' sprang to life, not recalling any such vacancy, but sure that if Mr Higson said that there was indeed a vacancy then there was one. "I believe we have," agreed 'Con'.
"Aren't the interviews on Wednesday," suggested Higson with the confident air of one who had just set up the interviews.
"I believe they could be," replied 'Con'.
"There, then, why don't you apply for the job? I'm sure 'Con' can arrange an interview for you Stan, it will help you with any extensions. Won't it?
Besides we can forget about the half day on Saturdays in the season if City are playing. We don't want you too tired to play, do we Stan?"
Stan's mind raced even faster than Harold Baker's but neither could detect a flaw in the offer - the club had not given in to Stan and Stan hadn't given in to the club, not yet. Higson had gained his man. "Think it over Stan. Don't rush. Talk it over with the wife and give 'Con' a ring tomorrow if you want to come," insisted Higson. Stan found himself rising from the chair with the words, "Right then, but I can't promise anything," coming involuntarily from his lips.
"Ask 'Arry to come up, Stan, please," shouted Mr. Baker.
The door swung behind Stan as he moved into the semi darkness of the stairs, alone with his thoughts.
"Higson can't bribe me," he muttered. Yet all the time, hanging at the back of his mind like a torn finger nail, were those kids in Fern Crescent - "Good game today Stan, you blinded Harris," they would shout. His workmates were expectant of a good result and a possible trip to Wembley. Somehow he knew he would be at the

interview on Wednesday and in the dressing room on Saturday, lacing up his boots in his own particular way, rubbing the resin onto his hands. "They always win, you can't beat 'em."

Behind the door Mr. Benjamin Higson was purring contentedly as he poured another large Gin for Harry Baker and placed it in front of him on the table. He offered a thin smile as he observed, "You know Harry you are too used to crushing cars between those sledgehammers of yours. You need the delicate strokes of a brush when dealing with sensitive players." Harold Baker grimaced back, satisfied that the deal was for the good of the club and looked up at the clock.

By now Stan had emerged into the glare of the arc lights of the training area but pushing the distant cries of "faster lads, legs up," into the back of his mind he searched out 'Arry in the kit room.

"'Arry you're wanted by the Gods," he shouted.

"Not going," beamed 'Arry.

"You'll be in trouble. Our Benjamin will be after your blood!"

"You must be joking. They'll be in trouble if nobody does these boots for Saturday."

"Well, I've done my job," said Stan, "You'd better go upstairs, they are waiting for you."

"They can wait," insisted 'Arry who immediately dispatched the luckless Sid to inform the Board of his decision.

With Stan's departure Mr. Higson had indeed been out for 'Arry's blood and, amid cries of "Who's running this bloody club, him or us? Bloody insulted, that's what I was," he was not far removed from a proposition that 'Arry be sacked. "There are plenty of other pensioners would give their right arm for his job," he declared. All had seemed lost for 'Arry until "Young" Taylor had declared that he had heard that, "we would have trouble from the players if 'Arry is removed. They think the world of him. We can't have that in cup week. The players' minds must only be on that cup match." Higson, sensing the possibility of a delicate situation arising conceded, "He'll have to apologise then before I go home from here tonight. He must learn who runs this bloody club."

The chairman, again looking at the clock and realising that such an apology from 'Arry would be equal to the whole board climbing the North face of Everest remarked, "I'll see 'Arry. That's what a chairman is for," and with Sid in tow he eagerly sought out 'Arry.

'Arry was to be found in the kit room where he was seated on a small three legged stool amid a mound of dirty boots, grass cuttings and discarded mud. At his elbow stood the second love of his life, his jewel box, an old red Elastoplast jar which contained a variety of assorted studs, all gathered by Sid from the pitch on past Monday mornings. With the end of a pair of pliers he gently tapped a stud into place to the accompaniment of "Too dear to keep buying new ones these days. The old leather ones never did anybody any harm."

"Hello 'Arry, just called to see if everything's all right for the cup match on Saturday," remarked Mr. Baker gingerly.

"Fine. Believe you want to see me. Haven't got much time you know. Must get these boots done tonight."

"No rush 'Arry, just called to let you know that Mr. Higson sends his apology for last Saturday. Would have called himself but he's had to rush off on some business. Bit of a misunderstanding really, 'Arry, he should know better. He hasn't been in the game as long as you and me, a lot to learn 'Arry."

"Aye, he has," replied 'Arry. With a sly grin on his face he added, "He'll not be pulling off any more door knobs then!"

"Anyway, glad to see everything's fine, 'Arry keep up the good work," commented Mr. Baker. Besides, he thought, "Where could we get two pit ponies and a donkey rolled into one for £25 pounds a week?"

Slowly he mounted the stairs and even more slowly did he cross the Boardroom floor to his seat, lighting a cigarette cupped in the palm of his hand.

"Well," asked Mr. Higson impatiently, "Did he send his apologies?"

Deliberately Mr. Baker drew upon his cigarette, settled into his chair and blew the smoke gently up into the air in Higson's direction. "Of course he did, he's terribly sorry about the incident. He hopes you'll forget the incident, Ben."

"How are the players?" snapped Higson.

"They're fine, Ben, and rarin to go. All talking about the Cup tie. You know Ben, you are right, it's surprising how a few strokes of the brush from an old master can suddenly alter the picture."

Harry Baker knows his players though. Mr. Higson doesn't, that's for sure. And I'm sure Stan Pearson would admit now that even he was wrong about Warren. Bates was the shrewdest signing City have made in years. Oh, not again. There must be a life somewhere without the telephone. You would think once the season is over then it would stop ringing. It doesn't. It'll be the Chairman, he said he'd ring at eleven o'clock. "No, Harry, there's nothing in the post from the Council. You could try ringing after the second delivery at one o'clock. But I think the Council will delay our request now that the Final is over. We should have put the request for an interest free loan before the Cup Final when the councillors were scrambling about for tickets. Yes, I agree with you, Harry, artificial turf would bring considerable income to the club in the summer months. Yes, no harm done in going down to Queens Park Rangers for a look at their pitch. What's the weather like? Good. Give me a ring about one o'clock then. Have a good holiday, Harry."

That's just like the Chairman, can't leave rugby alone. He takes his wife to Bournemouth for a fortnight and calls in at a soccer ground to inspect some artificial turf. I don't think he'll get any money out of the Council though. Still, if anybody can Harry Baker's the man. He did his party trick with Warren Bates when few clubs gave us a chance. He rarely fails when he sets his mind to it...

"Gone North"

Neither the twelve year old, hurriedly delivering his evening papers, along the full length of the even numbered houses in Carrs Close, Crynant, nor the council gardener making his way up the opposite side towards No 45 was aware how a small, brown, battered suitcase was to bring much confusion to the household inside. The twelve year old would read of its impact in his deliveries the next evening but the council gardener was soon to face the consequences for himself, his daughter in law, and especially his son, Warren Bates, Neath's goalkicking centre and currently the talk of the valley. The suitcase now lay open on the highly polished mahogany table in the living room at No 45 to reveal a collection of crisp twenty pound notes. Neatly bundled but falling out of the suitcase onto the table, they amounted to fifteen thousand pounds and, for the first time that day, they lay further than an arm's length away from Harry Baker, the Chairman. The brown case had, during that day, lay between Harry and Sam Cartwright on the back seat of Colin Taylor's Rover 2000 with all three excitedly aware of its destination.

As the car sped South their nervous chatter had subsided on leaving the M5 for the M50 and the Abergavenny Road, their silence only punctuated by remarks from Harry who indicated, for what seemed like the tenth time,

"There might be fog on the way back."

The open countryside passed by Harry, for, though peering through the rear window, his mind raced over the possibilities of capturing yet another big signing for City. His fingers had drummed incessantly on the brown lid of the case snuggling between him and Sam Cartwright whose sole observations on the surroundings had reflected his preoccupation with the game. "That's Monmouth School there, Colin. Keith Jarrett the Welsh international fullback came from there you know. A fine goalkicker, scored that famous try for Wales when he was only nineteen years old. We only missed him by a whisker. Barrow snatched him from under our noses before we could raise the money. Looks an old building. They must play on those pitches alongside."

Colin Taylor hardly noticed Monmouth School, never mind any grass alongside, as he kept his eyes firmly on the road to Neath and his mind on 'Tag' Potter's observation,

"He's the best there is. He'll be a sensation up North."

It had been City's chief scout in South Wales who had made the first exploratory contact with Warren in the Neath club lounge, following a fine game against Llanelli in the third round of the Welsh Cup. Warren had scored a try and kicked three goals in his side's victory but it was his sidestepping runs, allied to his dynamic tackling in the match which had earmarked him for the rugged demands so necessary in the league code. His qualities had been duly noted at the Dwr y Felin High School on countless Saturday mornings when, as a youngster, he had come under the shrewd eye of 'Tag' Potter. From his graduation through the Welsh schools team to the breaking of the Neath points scoring record Warren Bates' every skill had been noted, assessed and finally valued at £15,000 at only twenty-one years of age. Tag's initial overture to Warren in regard to the possibilities of playing league had been kindly received and, far from being removed from the clubhouse for a 'tar and feathering', he had enjoyed a pleasant chat for half an hour over a couple of pints. Warren was interested, even flattered, and Tag would certainly welcome his one per cent share (paid in the event of signings) if all went well with Mr. Baker's arrival in Carrs Close, Crynant.

The striking of a clock from somewhere in the hallway broke the silence within the bare living room. The sound seemed to reverberate around the room from the door to the mantelpiece on which stood Warren's photograph, taken when a proud schoolboy at the Cardiff Arms Park. Colin glanced at his watch which was showing half past six but he did not feel inclined to break Warren's studied concentration at the battered suitcase with its pile of notes scattered on the table.

"Here's Dad," called his wife Maureen from the kitchen. "There's the latch on the side gate. I'll let the tea brew for a minute. He likes it to be strong." Maureen had busied herself in the kitchen ever since the three directors had arrived, on the pretext of finishing the dishes whilst the men talked. She was now relieved that Warren's dad was coming to break the tension and opened the back door in anticipation of his entrance.

A thin, bowed and wiry figure rounded the corner of the house and entered at the back door whilst at the same time removing a black and red scarf from around his neck with hands, soiled by grime, yet revealing the jagged blue scars of coal dust from long ago. His scarf dislodged his cap to reveal a shock of black curly hair which made him look younger than his fifty-five years. An instinctive movement of his left hand allowed him to catch the falling cap before it reached the floor and, throwing it and the scarf over the peg behind the door, his mouth burst into a grin which highlighted the broken bone in his nose.

"Nearly knocked on there. Now, what's up? Must be something important to ring me at the depot. Ted Carter thought I had a fancy woman up my sleeve. No such luck though." Taking a small brown paper bag from his corduroy jacket he tipped the remains of the tea leaves into the caddy on the window sill.

"Didn't get a chance for a brew this afternoon, was clearing trees
in Jackson Street."

Maureen smiled and kissed him on the cheek, indicating with a
raising of her eyebrows and a nod of the head in the direction of
the living room that his presence was required inside. With a grin
and a wink of his eye to reassure Maureen, he replaced the lid of
the tea caddy, picked up a wheatmeal biscuit from the glass jar at
its side and slowly but deliberately strode into the living room,
trailing blades of grass from his shoes onto the brown patterned
carpet. As if drawn by a magnet, his eyes settled on the twenty
pound notes lying in the open suitcase and his jaw sagged slightly
to allow a few crumbs from his wheatmeal biscuit to drop gently
to the floor from the side of his mouth. He stared in disbelief,
hardly noticing the occupants of the room, least of all Harry
Baker who was scrutinising his every move, fully aware how vital
was Mr. Bates in any capture of his son Warren. Slowly dad
recovered his full vision and as the remainder of the room came
into full focus his eyes were freed from the suitcase on the table.
Harry Baker, sat in the armchair near the fire, Colin Taylor,
seated on one of the straight backed chairs at the table, and Sam
Cartwright, sat upright on the edge of the russet settee, all met
his gaze.

"Dad, these gentlemen are from up North in the rugby league.
They want me to sign for their club for a lot of money,"
interrupted Warren, rising from his seat on the settee alongside
Sam Cartwright.

"I can see that," replied dad, gaining his composure. "Have you
made them a cup of tea?"

"Maureen's making one for us all. She's been waiting until you
came home. This is Mr. Baker, Mr. Taylor, and Mr. Cartwright dad."
All three leapt to their feet in turn to shake hands while dad

excused the grime on his hands with,

"Been clearing fallen trees today. The wind's been a bloody nuisance."

"As you know, dad, Mr. Baker wants me to sign for City. They've offered fifteen thousand pounds. Ten thousand pounds now, three after one season, and another two thousand after two seasons play. What do you think?"

"Nowt to do with me lad, it's your life. You owe your dad nothing."

"It's a lot of money dad."

"It bloody is, that's for sure!" he replied as his eyes flickered yet again over the brown magnet on the table - a magnet which to him represented years of work down the pit and even more years of work now that he had been invalided to the Parks and Gardens Department with the Council. The notes lay there in bundles, toppling out of the case just like the piles of autumnal leaves he had swept away from the fallen trees that afternoon.

"Should these fallen leaves be collected or swept away, possibly never to be seen again," he mused to himself.

"Mr. Simpson thinks I might win a Welsh cap," suggested Warren, as if trying to break the old man's silence. "He's heard I might be picked. When I mentioned the offer to him he said that I might not like rugby league, that I wouldn't enjoy it. He thought there was little social life like there is at the Neath club, that I would miss all the lads. Money's not everything, dad." Warren was vainly trying to put a not too convincing argument together for not signing, as if in defence of the traditional Welsh hostility, but the remarks of club committee man Hector Simpson certainly stirred dad.

"It's not everything to him, lad, to Terry Simpson. He has three electrical shops and a Cash and Carry in the town centre. Will he pay for your social life after the matches? What happens if you

*"His eyes settled on the
Twenty Pound notes lying
in the suitcase"*

break your leg next week and are out of the game? He'll still be in his committee seat at the Gnoll whether you are playing or not. Will he pay the rent here? No, money's not everything to Terry Simpson."

"We're half way there," thought Colin Taylor. Harry Baker lit a cigarette and, seeing no ash tray, flicked his ash into the matchbox, an act which he intensely disliked but felt that silence was for the better at this vital stage.

"Some of that money would help to look after your dad, Warren," suggested Colin Taylor.

"Doesn't need to sign for me, he'll need to look after Maureen and himself, not me. I'm fine here," snapped dad, as the first signs of any antagonism flashed across his face.

"Bloody idiot," thought Harry Baker. "What did I bring him for. No idea of handling a signing. Too bloody young, no experience." Harry's mind raced to restore the calm and, as Maureen placed a tray containing five cups, sugar bowl, milk jug, and a tea pot on the table, he asked, "What does Maureen think about it all?"

Harry's years of experience were now telling him to switch the attention from dad and let him settle. When you sign a player you sign his wife first.

"I don't mind going North but it's up to Warren. There's not much here, Mr. Baker, and Mr. Cartwright has said that he'll help us to find a nice house."

"Don't worry Maureen, we'll attend to everything. That's our job. All our Welsh players have settled in well in the past. In fact, I think you already know Colin Rees' wife. He really enjoyed his rugby with us."

"Good move, Sam, an old trooper," thought Harry.

"She's a nice girl is Elaine," observed Maureen, instantly recalling their school days as, pouring milk into the cups, she added, "she used to be our form prefect when I was in the first year at school." "If you pay all the fee at once I'll sign," suggested Warren boldly, yet looking in the direction of his father as if seeking support for such a forthright statement.

"Well, I'll probably get the sack from the board," laughed Harry, "but I'll offer £12,000 now and £3,000 at the end of the season. I'll stick my neck out, Warren, I think I know an honest player when I see one. I'll risk it." Sam Cartwright's eyebrows raised ever so slightly at the thought of Harry Baker risking anything, especially as both well knew that he had the authority from the City board to go as high as £15,000 cash if it was necessary. Harry was bluffing but he was playing his aces early in the deal for he sensed that he was nearly there. He eased back into his chair, contented with his progress.

"Are you sure what you want to do, Warren?" asked dad.

A cautionary note suddenly flashed across Harry's face as Colin Taylor began to stir at the table.

"For Christ's sake, don't open your mouth Colin, let it ride," thought Harry.

"Once I've taken the money, there's no going back, is there?" pleaded Warren. "Am I doing right Maureen?"

Maureen shirked the responsibility, did not reply, but duly placed the sugar bowl on the table. A full minute elapsed when all in the living room averted their eyes from another's gaze, none eager to speak. The time had come. 'The area of the great self doubt,' thought Harry and rose to begin to replace the notes neatly in the suitcase. Dad looked at the faded photograph of his dead wife on the mantelpiece then across at Warren's. A whole generation was to flash across his mind - the hard days at the pit, that accident, his own playing days at Blaina. His inner instincts came to the fore and the bitterness which invariably lies beneath the miner's skin bubbled over.

"Take it lad. Nobody in Neath will look after you when you are too old to play. You'll still have to pay for your own ale then. Mr. Simpson will be buying it for a new Warren Bates then. It's your decision lad, but I'd take it."

"Do what you want Warren, I don't mind," interrupted Maureen. She filled the cups and spoke in a hushed voice without looking at Warren as if half afraid to urge her husband too far.

Harry stubbed his cigarette in the matchbox, retired back to the chair and comforted himself with the pleasant thought,

"We're there."

"Give me the forms Mr. Baker and I'll sign."

Contrary to expectations Harry Baker eased further back into his armchair and merely waved an indicating arm in the general direction of Sam Cartwright who, until now, had played a somewhat minor role. Suddenly Sam, like a well oiled retainer, slid his hand onto the leather briefcase which he had deposited at the side of the settee. In a moment the briefcase was on his knees and, burrowing amid sheafs of papers, he emerged with the necessary registration forms. A silver pen had appeared between the fingers of his right hand, as if by magic, and rather in the fashion of the old gunslinger who used to keep a small firearm up his sleeve for surprise. The pen was instantly transferred to Warren's left hand; registration forms were placed under it on the mahogany table to receive the shaky but legible signature of WARREN BATES.

Maureen looked on and beamed at Colin, proud of her Warren and dreaming of rows and rows of large detached houses, all with large lawns at the back. Colin Taylor too looked on, not daring to say anything whilst Harry Baker drew his fingers over his eyes. It had been a tiring day for Harry and he was not looking forward to the journey back home that night. Still, he had bagged his catch. Dad, content that the lad's future was assured, reached for a cup of tea prepared for him on the tray. He grimaced at the taste of too much sugar and, whilst all the attention was on the signing, replaced the cup and tried another to his satisfaction.

"Welcome to City," said Colin Taylor and immediately thrust his hand forward to greet Warren's, once the signing was completed. Turning his gaze once again to the mound of notes in the suitcase Warren picked up a bundle, turned it over and, replacing it neatly on top, remarked,

"I don't feel happy with these in the house overnight. I wouldn't like to be responsible for taking them to the bank in the morning."

"Never mind," chipped in Harry, now rising from his chair. "We'll look after these for you. I'll get Sam to sign a cheque instead. We'll take these back with us. It'll be much easier for you."

Warren nodded his approval. The display had worked. Harry always liked to use the suitcase. It would be back in the Midland Bank by 10.30 in the morning. In fact he had previously arranged for Con Chapman to pick it up at half past nine from his house.

"Let's have a cup of tea," insisted Maureen excitedly. "Though I think we should have champagne from the Mitre. Is it too early? Will they be open yet?" She glanced at the clock on the wall but her questioning was abruptly ended with,

"Champagne? Dai has no champagne, only vintage Brown Ale!" Dad laughed aloud and concluded, "Tea will have to do, I don't think Mr. Baker's bothered."

Harry indicated his more than willing acceptance of a cup of tea and soon all drank with a feeling of relief - Warren cupping his hand around the mug and staring at the brown liquid, as if seeking assurance in the leaves which were floating on top. With

Colin Taylor indicating to Warren the need to gain full publicity
in the evening and daily papers on the Saturday and Sunday to
ensure a bumper gate on the Monday evening, Sam and Harry
straightened the notes in the case. They replaced the lid and
placed the suitcase alongside the briefcase near the settee. Their
work done, Harry reassured Warren that his debut would be
better in the first team on the Monday rather than the 'A' team
on the Saturday.

"You can have a watching session with the lads on Saturday and a
brief run through a few things on the Sunday morning. You must
bring Maureen with you, let her look at a few houses over the
weekend. You can stay at the Breckinridge in town."

"I'd love that," said Maureen, now linking her arm inside
Warren's at the table.

"Are you sure I'll be okay in the first team on Monday? I've only
seen the game on television. I don't want to let you all down."

"Don't worry," reassured Colin Taylor, "you'll be alright on
the night."

'No fear,' thought Harry Baker, 'Big publicity, big crowd - if you
are going to flop 'boyo', flop in front of a fifteen thousand crowd,
not two thousand. It's cheaper. We should get half the fee back
on Monday night.'

Yes, it was a long journey home, probably be about two o'clock in
the morning when they got in. Harry wasn't looking forward to
the trip but somehow he knew that he would settle in the back
seat and dream up a quote for the press. Yes, he'd pulled off
another big one! He couldn't wait for Monday..........

..........With only ten minutes left to play before the final whistle
Warren Bates reflected upon Colin Taylor's words,

"You'll be alright on the night," and indeed he did feel 'alright'
within himself. Colin's predictions had rung true for a fourteen

thousand crowd had packed the City ground, all eagerly awaiting the 7.15pm kick off and the emergence from the tunnel of what they all hoped would be their new 'superstar'. As on all such occasions, there had been a tingle of excitement on the terraces and from Club Chairman down to old aged pensioner all willed their Welsh capture to succeed. A few old timers in the paddock stand on the Abbey Road side had already talked Warren into the forthcoming Great Britain side for the tour of Australia. On stepping onto the pitch Warren had become aware instinctively that over fourteen thousand pairs of eyes waited for the first sidestep, a creative run, the first goalkick or the first crunching tackle - something to roar at, something to gloat over.

The first crunching tackle did come within the first minute, though it was executed upon himself with a sickening thud by Oldham's stocky inside centre Harry Osborne. It certainly had the effect of knocking any wrapping paper from City's new product for, on receiving a much slower ball from the scrum than he had been used to in Union, he was unceremoniously upended and dumped to the ground by Harry who had moved in defence very quickly. The crisply laundered red and white striped jersey was streaked with mud; the white shorts now had a black patch on the thigh where originally was emblazoned his position No 3 in bold red lettering. The glamour of posing for photographs on the club steps, the cosy weekend with Maureen at the Breckinridge Hotel had all been dumped on the floor in one tackle. Here was a new game to play and learn, a new reputation to be made as players like Harry Osborne strove mightily to make their reputations at Warren's expense - an expense of fifteen thousand pounds to City. But things were 'alright on the night' for with the minutes creeping away he could look back on a steady game in which he had given the spectators an indication of his ability to sidestep, his eagerness to make a tackle, and, above all, he had shown himself to be in good form with his kicking, landing two from the touchline in City's 12pts to 7pts win. He had achieved little of the spectacular but he had earned the respect of the players around him whilst he himself had been brought down to earth by the skills arrayed around him. The tricky play of Stan Pearson at stand off, whose clever running had found the gaps in Oldham's defence for Warren to make use of, had excited him. The strength of Mac, City's seventeen stones prop forward, had amazed him, especially Mac's ability to be in the right place at the right time for the scoring of his two tries. Mac's ability to be 'in the right place at the right time' however had little to do with the fact that he was completing his 350th game for the club but that with his Testimonial function to follow the match he had been keeping out of the way. His frequent appearances out towards the wings, as opposed to the centre of the field, the normal preserve of the forwards, brought him two tries from what appeared to be clever support play. However, Mac's eyes had been on the clock and, noting that the lights were going on in the Cabaret Lounge behind the scoreboard for the commencement of a "Gentlemens Evening" he had sought to avoid too much trouble on the field. Having been awarded a Testimonial benefit season for his ten years service to City, Monday night was the culmination of a year's hard graft of lotteries, socials and dinners by which he and his committee of players and supporters had sought to raise for him a bumper financial reward. Tonight's last function would top the target of two thousand pounds and Mac had too many figures, ticket sales, and bills to be paid, revolving around his head to get himself too caught up in the heat of forward play. Nor would he look good in the local press receiving his cheque at the end of tonight's function with a black eye or broken nose.

When the final whistle did arrive it was with a sense of relief that both Warren and Mac, once they had made their way through the back slapping throng of children, sought the comfort of the bath. For Warren it was the relief at not being totally exposed in the professional code and the relief that inside himself he knew that he would make the grade. For Mac it was a relief to get off the pitch in order to concentrate on his important matter for the night, namely the Gentleman's Evening. The soft soapy water soon covered Warren's body as he lay outstretched on the bottom of the bath, his head only emerging above the water to chat with Stan Pearson and Peter Todd alongside him. Far more than by the water Warren was warmed inwardly by the pleasant congratulations which he received from such players who pointed out where he had gone wrong, but who were also quick to praise his strong points during the game. A few quips from his opposition centre, Harry Osborne, as to his financial capabilities of "lending me a few bob" brought him more warmth. He lingered in the deep, communal bath, applying the soft soothing soap to his body and emptying the last dripping contents of his shampoo sachet playfully into the hairs on his chest. He was happy, he was content, and especially so when Harry Baker leaned over the bath side. Parting the rising steam with his arm he had given the thumbs up signal to Warren and had accompanied it with, "Good 'un tonight, Warren," and added jokingly, "thought you could kick goals."

Warren, self-consciously, gave a wry smile, then slid under the water to remove all the clinging soap and shampoo from his body. On emerging he could see the huge shape of Mac, already in the dressing room, endeavouring to open a can of pale ale at the same time as putting on his shoes, whilst his back was being

rubbed down by the ever faithful Sid. The rubbing of his back by
Sid and the manoeuvering of his shoes at his heel caused him to
spill his ale down his trousers - an action which was greeted by
one of his assorted oaths, the snatching of the towel from Sid, and
a rebuke from 'Arry for the use of foul language in his dressing
room. But Mac, having only dipped lightly into the bath, was in a
hurry to be dressed. Though even he could not move upstairs to
the Cabaret Lounge until he had found his shorts from the pile
on the floor to give to 'Arry for the wash. With his hands now
dirtied from rummaging on the floor for his shorts he joked that
he was doing 'Arry's job and should be paid accordingly.
"If I'd done your job tonight Mac," retorted 'Arry, "I'd have been
ashamed to collect my wages for what you did."
"You tell him 'Arry," roared Len Topping the coach.
"Scored the winning try didn't I?" grinned Mac.
"Could have scored that one myself, even with Sid playing inside
me," snapped 'Arry, grabbing Sid by the collar and propelling
him in the direction of the kit room.
"We've work to do. We can't go ogling females," was 'Arry's final
comment as he and Sid left to prepare to scrape the boots. Mac,
adjusting his tie, made his way back to the bath to dip his hands,
now dirtied, into the water and, leaning over, asked Warren, "Will
you make the draw for me, Warren? It would be a nice touch for
the supporters if you would."
Warren, still playing the game over in his mind, was eager to
accept and, keen to become one of the team as quickly as
possible, raised himself from the water, rubbed a last dirt stain
from his thigh and, turning full frontal to face Mac,
innocently replied,
"Do you want me now?"
Mac laughed and, effecting an exaggerated lisp, replied,

"No thanks dearie. You're not my type. My God we are getting a
lot for our £15,000." He grinned wide and added, "No, ten
o'clock will do, after the buffet. Come up and see the show. It
should interest an innocent sheep like you from the valleys."
The term 'Cabaret Lounge' was rather a grandiose title to apply
to the red plastic topped tables which stood in rows upstairs in the
long narrow room. With a bar running the length of one side
where the entrance door was sited, the only other feature was a
small half circular stage at the far corner of the room, just big
enough to accommodate a drum kit, small organ, a microphone,
and the ever faithful Bingo machine. From these boards a never
ending supply of fifteen pounds a time comics and singers had
belted out their gags and songs as a prelude to the nightly calling
of the magical Bingo numbers. This constant supply of
excitement filled the lounge on most nights.

By ten o'clock however the stage had been cleared, save the
precious Bingo numbers drum which had been placed to the rear,
in anticipation of receiving the exotic Carla, the oriental dancer
from Wigan. Carla was booked to titillate the palates of the all
male audience for the princely sum of fifty pounds for two dances
which would be performed in accompaniment with Mac's club tie
and a flat cap seized from the head of an unsuspecting pensioner
in the front row of the tables. The room was by now bursting to
the seams as players, supporters, and itinerant voyeurs crowded
the tables, stood on the chairs, and thronged around the stage to
await the delights of Wigan in the flesh. At £5 a ticket inclusive of
buffet and cabaret, Mac had done well and, anticipating a
considerable financial return for the night's work, he was in no
mood to listen to the pleas of Carla's husband and manager who
was whimpering vainly at his side. Mac towered like a colossus at
the side of the stage and guarded Carla's dressing room door, or,

more appropriately, the Lottery Development Office Kiosk.
Carla's husband at Mac's side resembled a small, bald garden
gnome, lacking only his fishing rod. Clad in a maroon velvet
jacket and bright red tie, his bald head glistened under the
spotlights and beads of sweat dripped from his forehead as he
urgently appealed to Mac to keep the crowds back from the stage,
and especially the Lottery Development door.

The crowd however surged forward at Carla's entrance and, amid
scenes reminiscent of the Yukon trail, her bottom and bouncing
breasts became the target for every stray hand. Her husband's
head disappeared beneath the melee which swept forward as she
made her way onto the stage. His complaints could only faintly
be heard from his position near the floor, where, on losing
control of his feet, he was heard to shriek at the behaviour of the
management and the customers. Most of the customers were
oblivious to his complaints and with Mac representing the
management he was greeted with the usual assortment of friendly
remarks, culminating in the all embracing greeting for such
occasions, "Piss off!"

"You're lucky you haven't been grabbed yourself, mate. I thought
it was all in for fifty pounds. Nothing like trying the goods before
buying them," insisted Mac.

During Carla's exotic dances, in which the audience were
painfully to realise the obstructive uses to which a flat cap could
be put, the bar had been shut and the metal grille lowered into
position temporarily in order to allow the Bar staff a little time to
clean the glasses. Seizing his chance to gain a better view and
never one to miss an opportunity when sex reared its head, Sid
had climbed on to the bar top from the inside and clung to the
metal security grille. Clinging to this position he peered at Carla
as a chimpanzee in the zoo until, on the completion of her act, he

made attempts to extricate himself from the grille. Unfortunately in his eagerness and frenzy to view every last second of the climax to the dances he had stuck his fingers into the grille and was now unable to remove them from the metallic links. The customers' attentions were now turning back to the bar and the sight of Sid, suspended from the inside of the grille and seemingly in the act of crucifixion, did little to quench the thirsts of the frustrated mob surging around. The requests to have the security grille removed mounted appreciably when Sid's predicament was explained by the harassed bar staff. Despite the removal of a considerable amount of skin from his knuckles, in his successful attempt to remove himself, Sid received little sympathy. Rather he became the butt of the players' taunts.

"Exhibitionist. Stone the bastard!" were amongst the choice Biblical allusions which were immediately forthcoming from Stan Pearson. Such comments rang around the Bar until Mac, sensing the predicament, announced as a diversion, that buffet was available in the side room for all those with tickets.

Such was the stampede for the door adjoining the two rooms that it was rumoured that only prop forwards actually obtained any food, all the remainder being content with the sight of a paper plate and a plastic fork between two. All that is, save Len Topping the coach and a master sidestepping winger in his day, who always advocated the use of brain rather than brawn. Sensing the crush Len had nipped, at great speed, through the Gents and through the Lottery Office door to emerge in the adjoining room at the head of the throng where he was found to have helped himself to his full quota of chicken legs and hot pie. Brushing aside a few choice comments as to the size of his appetite he returned via the Gents to await the prize, delighting in 'Arry's parting shot,

"You can still sidestep around these thick forwards, eh, Len."

A large Golden Wonder crisp box, containing the assorted pink, green, and yellow tickets for the 'grand draw' had been placed on the stage on top of the portable television, donated by Ben Higson. Standing alongside Warren he awaited the draw somewhat impatiently whilst Carla's husband, pathetically complaining that he would report the club to Equity, searched in vain for her bra which had mysteriously disappeared from the floor at the close of her act. His futile search concluded, both he and Carla fled the club back to Wigan, followed by cries of, "I've seen better legs on Mac. There's more bounce in the City front row."

Indeed that night there was bounce in the front row, for Mac had achieved his final target and could relax after ten seasons play to enjoy the extra benefit his testimonial had brought. For Warren, about to make the draw and listening to Ben Higson's introductory speech, he had already received his financial benefit but was eager to earn it and indeed, he expressly hoped that his career too would last ten seasons.

*Just look at this office. No one would ever suspect we were a first class
club. Whoever bought this desk must have done a deal with Noah when
he was looking for wood for his Ark. It's a good job that BARLA make
their handbook so thick. It makes up for the loss of that castor on the right
leg. And that filing cabinet was rescued from Burtonwood when the
Yanks pulled out after the war. What a colour, green and brown! Must
be camouflage from the war. It's certainly got character.*

*And you don't get characters like that man in the game now. Always
used to dive for his tries did Albert Proudlove. Fifty-three tries in
1956/57 season. That's the best picture I've seen of Albert, taken against
Halifax I think. From the same town as Warren Bates. Neath.
Lightning must strike twice. That pile of brochures on top of the cabinet
will have to be thrown out now that Mac has finished his testimonial. I
can't see us selling any more of these in the summer. Two good signings,
Albert and Warren.*

*"You win some and you lose some," as Sam Cartwright never tires of
saying. Or at least his brother in law should say after what he did to Sam
this season...*

"City Centre"

Two o'clock. The strike of the station clock caused Carl Geraghty to look out of the taxi window and back at the crowded forecourt where a small group of boys were eagerly discussing his exit. "Plenty of time. We'll be there in five minutes," assured Sam Cartwright leaning back in the soft padded seat alongside him, obviously enjoying the attention. Carl had felt most important when Mr. Cartwright, resplendent in his bright red City blazer, had greeted him at the station gate. Eyes had turned in his direction, conversations had ceased, when the ticket collector, sensing the urgency and possible importance, had waved him through the barrier with an approving nod at Sam Cartwright. Inside the darker corner of the taxi however he felt most insecure, though not nervous, and wondered to himself why he had been plucked from the Yorkshire Amateur League Division Three for a trial for City. And in the first team, not the 'A' team! Though admittedly against weak opposition. Sam waved at a passer by through the window as if he were royalty bringing home a foreign dignitary for all to see, then turned as if reassuringly to Carl.

"My brother in law is a good judge of a player. He's doing grand work for City since his job took him to Huddersfield. He certainly liked your play in that match against ...er ...er"

"Fearnsides, Mr Cartwright."

"Aye that's it, Fearnsides. We need stylish centres in this game today. Got a good eye for a footballer. Got your name from a spectator. Said you were as good a No. 4 as he had seen in amateur rugby."

"But I.........."

"No 'buts'," interrupted Sam, "have confidence in yourself.
There's a lot of money to be earned in this game today for the
successful player."

Sam's brother in law, though somewhat short sighted, prided
himself on his ability to spot a young 'good un' and, though now
far removed from his beloved City club, took it upon himself to
scour the local Yorkshire amateur leagues for talent.

"Must still do my bit for City, you know Sam. No, I won't hear of
expenses. If I can continue to produce internationals for the club
then I'm happy."

No one at the City club, and especially Sam, could actually
remember a future international ever being recommended to the
club by his brother in law but no club could ever afford to turn
away a recommendation. After all, hadn't Wigan had first choice
of Stan Pearson all those years ago and turned him down?

"This lad's going to be a blinder. Lovely sidestep and fine turn of
speed," Sam's brother in law had insisted over the telephone.
Best No 4 I've seen in amateur rugby. Got his name and address
off a spectator so nobody else would know City were interested
in him."

Sam had learned to treat his brother in law's observations with
more than a little diffidence but even he dare not let the catch off
the hook. If Carl Geraghty were to prove a big fish then this
capture would stand Sam in good stead at the Annual General
Meeting when he was up for re-election. And besides, with his
brother in law now safely tucked away in Huddersfield amid
virtual anonymity, then this lad was to be Sam's own signing.
Before Carl could reflect on whether he had played at No. 3 or
No. 4 on the day in question the taxi drew up at the ground
outside the Players Entrance, an entrance flanked by two mock
portals above which were inscribed the letters CITY R.L.F.C. in

red but below which was scrawled "rubbish" in green aerosol spray paint. The faithful guardian of the entrance stood to one side, in his hands a bundle of envelopes containing complimentary tickets for players' wives, friends, and relatives, ever watchful that no one slipped by without his assent. Surely serving his apprenticeship for Heaven's gates! The taxi was engulfed by a horde of youngsters, clad in a variety of red and white scarves, hats, and badges which caused Sam Cartwright a little inconvenience in opening the rear door. However, on stepping out of the car, he waved a path through and, thrusting out his chest, he commented to no one in particular, but obviously designed for the ears of the doorkeeper,

"A good 'un from Yorkshire. We've done well to get this lad."
The doorman beamed at Carl as he fumbled for his kit bag which had fallen to the floor and was retrieved by a young girl, now leaning on the taxi. Muttering his thanks, he strode forward to be greeted at the door by Len Topping who had left the team dressing room, deliberately, to be on hand to welcome him to the club. Len offered a strong handshake to Carl who accepted it rather limply, now suddenly overawed by the occasion and wishing that the ground might swallow him up.

"Don't worry, lad, play your normal game. The lads will look after you. Do you want shoulder pads? I'll get some for you from 'Arry."
Before Carl could offer an answer he was guided away to the Home dressing room by Len's friendly arm on his shoulder where he was greeted by an array of faces, some of which he had seen on television and in the newspapers. Others he recognised from his many trips as a youngster to Fartown at Huddersfield and now felt a little guilty at having booed them from the terraces. But all wished him well, in particular Stan Pearson who, in the act of removing his top teeth with one hand and applying vaseline to his

eyebrows with the other, urged him to "follow me and keep close in defence."

"You won't go far wrong, son", encouraged Mac.

"Don't get hurt," urged Tony Smith, "I could do with a rest today." The trialist turned towards the player and offered a weak smile not knowing the implications behind the statement. The last thing Tony Smith wanted was to rest on the substitutes bench but he had little choice in the matter. The tight feeling in the pit of Tony Smith's stomach had begun on Thursday evening when the team sheet had been pinned to the wall of the team dressing room. To be listed as a substitute, after several seasons as a first team regular, and to read the name of A.N. Other in his place, came as an unwelcome shock to Tony and one that he had found difficult to accept. However, hiding his true feelings, he had accepted the lot of the professional, but it was with mixed feelings that he now viewed Mr A.N. Other or Carl Geraghty pulling on his jersey.

Meanwhile Ben Higson had arrived in the dressing room, taking great care not to soil his new suede coat, tightly belted at the waist, on the patches of powdered resin lying on the benches.

"You're Sam's lad, aren't you?"

"Why did he speak so loud?" thought Carl.

"Hope you can justify his faith in you, lad. Heard a lot about you from Mr. Cartwright. He's rarely wrong in his assessment of a player is Sam," observed Mr. Higson, looking pointedly in the direction of Sam Cartwright who had now appeared at the door in order to give a final nod of approval to Carl. Ben Higson turned to leave and, disappearing down the corridor with Sam Cartwright, remarked,

"He's a bag of bones, Sam"

"Charlie Acland only weighed nine stones but he was the best full back this club has ever had," retorted Sam defiantly.

"He'll need to be a good player with those knees. Like bloody doorstops! Still, we'll see soon.. It's only Rochdale we're playing. Nothing at stake is there?" Higson concluded.

Though Carl mumbled his thanks to every wellwisher, the words of encouragement hardly registered in a mind focussing on the three o'clock kick off and grappling with the implications of 'the best No. 4 he'd seen'. Surely he had played as No. 3 against Fearnsides. Hadn't Colin Parkin moved from stand off to No. 4 when Alan Harris cried off? He couldn't recall. No, but he needed little thought to recall later his experience between 3pm and 3.40pm of that afternoon. He had failed to take crucial passes, had appeared in the wrong places at the wrong time and had failed to appreciate the speed of his opposite number who had sped past him for two tries. He had hoped, ever since the letter had arrived through the post inviting him to a trial, that he would be good enough to make the transition from the amateur ranks to the professional. Ever unsure of himself, he had informed no one of the trial in the event of him being a failure. He had wondered as to why he had been singled out of the Staincliffe side and why no Colin Parkin. Surely Colin was the best player in the club. Nevertheless, his confidence was not exactly brimming over as he sought his seat on the bench in the dressing room at half time to listen to the harangue of Len Topping explaining the reasons for a "so called professional side" being ten points behind against "a bunch of bloody amateurs". Carl Geraghty or A.N. Other wished the ground would swallow him up. Not so Tony Smith.

Indeed, for the first time in the last forty eight hours since he had made his way disconsolately home from the training session, there had been a spring in Tony's step as he eased himself from the

"reduced to the job of carrying the tracksuits and the medical bag from the pitch at half-time"

hard wooden seat to lean forward from the concrete dugout, the home of the substitutes, trainers, and coaches during the match. The dark clouds gathering over the main stand on the far side of the pitch had caused Tony to tighten the towel around his neck, as if in anticipation of the rain they seemed about to bring. Throughout the first half he had not felt the cold and had been unmoved by the swirls and gusts of wind which played around the dugout, but had watched with glazed eyes the players suffer their humiliation. Tony had observed the play with the cynicism usually reserved for a professional who, at the age of thirty three years, not only wonders but knows that he is approaching the end of his career. He had needed a rest. His back had been playing him up for some weeks. He had deliberately kept quiet about it, not wishing to miss the prospect of any bumper pay packets, and preferring to treat the injury at home with a rather ineffective Heat Lamp bought many years earlier for his mother's arthritis. The treatment, like the lamp, had also proved ineffective but the enforced rest was now not to Tony's liking, especially after seven years of uninterrupted play for the City first team. He felt shame at sitting on the bench. He, Tony Smith, one of the best in the league, reduced to the job of carrying the tracksuits and the medical bag from the pitch at half time. He, who had covered every blade of grass or whatever blades of grass were left after the January mud, forced to make only the short walk across the pitch back to the tunnel. Why did he have to cross the pitch in front of the large crowd? Tony had concentrated on the comments rolling down above the spectators' heads, seemingly from the back of the terraces, for he could place no distinctive face to any of the shouts hurled in his direction.

"Get changed Tony. That pack's bloody hopeless."

"Ask for a move Smithy if you're not better than that lot. Topping wants his head seeing to."

"Where did they get that bloody centre from? Mothercare?"

Such comments gave him encouragement with which to enter the
darkness of the tunnel. He even allowed himself a grin as he left
the field, perhaps the only contented player to enter the dressing
room to listen to Len Topping's expected harangue, and, though
concerned for the welfare of the City team and their attempts to
salvage some respect from the match, he was more concerned
with his own position and the temporary loss of his earning
capacity. Or was he? His pride was the real issue at stake.

Amid a pause in Len's flowing oratory Higson entered and, in the
act of wiping his hands on the towel lying on the table at the side
of Len, he whispered,

"Get the lad off Len. We've seen enough. Put Smith in the
forwards. He needs a run for fitness. And bring Todd out of the
pack to centre." Replacing the towel he strode straight to Carl,
shook him on the shoulder and said, "Well done Geraghty. You
showed promise there. Have a rest for this half. Let Smith earn
his wages," before turning on his heel and back out of the
dressing room. Like a fly on the wall Carl listened to the harsh
words from the coach but he noted how few of the players
seemed to be listening.

The noise had eased. Len's tirade had subsided. The players
were now concentrating and chatting quietly about the difficult
task ahead in the second half. Emotions had been released on
both sides. The head was now beginning to rule the heart again.

"Put a few kicks in on the fourth tackle when their wingers are
still lying up. Don't let Atkins keep playing the ball to the blind
side. Somebody get him chopped before he can move,"
suggested Len.

Tony surveyed the dressing room from the relative safety of the side room. He was part of the team again, yet free of the general censure on their play of the first forty minutes. The same pegs, the same bright red woodwork which peeped out beneath the assorted jackets, suede coats and trousers had been there when Tony started two hundred and thirty games ago. They would be there too, holding similar coats and jackets, long after Tony had gone. But he was happy again.

As the players filed out for the second half, to be followed by 'Arry carrying the sponge bag and a spare red tracksuit, Carl found himself alone in the silence of the dressing room save the sound of the water from the hot taps running slowly into the large bath. Steam, which was slowly rising from the few inches of water already in the bath, floated through the open door into the changing room as if fog was about to envelop him.

What should he do? Get changed? Wait in the dressing room or go back out onto the pitch? He looked at the table in the middle of the floor - at the bottle of olive oil, now cold, and at the red Elastoplast tin full of vaseline from which fingers had gouged huge lumps to apply to varied ears, eyebrows, noses or elbows. The powdered resin, for the hands, lay loose at the end of the table where it had been poured too liberally from the Johnson's Baby Powder tin which acted as its dispenser. All was still, the emotion had left the room and its contents, now discarded, were isolated from the action on the field. Carl too had been discarded but he was embarrassed not so much by his inadequacy on the field but with his inadequacy of mind as to what to do with himself now. He longed to hide under the bench but it was not to be, for Sam Cartwright, after hurried consultations with Harry Baker, had made his way from the Directors Box in the main stand. First visiting the telephone in the secretary's office, he approached the dressing room where his steps on the stone corridor floor startled Carl into looking up.

"Hard going Carl? You look as if you were enjoying it, anyway." Before Carl could reply Sam gripped his arm as in a handshake, pressed a brown envelope into his hand and added,

"You've done well. Here's a few pounds for some expenses for you. If you hurry you'll catch the 4.20 train. Taxi's outside. All the best, lad. We'll be in touch with you. Must dash." His goodbye delivered, Sam Cartwright hurriedly left Carl sitting on the bench. Carl was to be no Hair shirt for Sam Cartwright to wear. To Sam, the sooner this particular shirt was taken from his back the better.

With the match still in progress, when he had dressed, few saw him leave via the players' entrance where even the gateman had deserted his post. He threw his kit onto the back seat of the waiting Taxi and climbed in. Here he was thankfully spared the embarrassment of the same driver and the need to communicate an explanation to him on the way back so early to the station. The crumpled brown envelope dropped from his hand to the car floor as, unconsciously, he placed the two ten pound notes into his top pocket alongside the rail ticket, thinking to himself,

"I was No. 3, Colin Parkin had played at 4. Still it doesn't matter now."

There was no 'waving through' at the station ticket barrier on the return trip for he was forced to join a small queue forming to await the ticket collector who strode past him without recognition. The queue shuffled forward. He kicked his kit bag a few feet further forward along the floor. Carl noted the makers name on the station clock above him and quietly consoled himself with the thought,

"Yes, I was in the No. 3 jersey. They got the wrong man. Well, at least I'll be home for six o'clock."

I think that brochure for the gymnasium can go in the bin too, no reason to spend four thousand pounds when the Council can do it for you. Ben Higson's right when he says,
"Open the facilities up to the public during the day and we can get a grant for the gymnasium."
The trouble is if they come from Carforth Council estate we'll have no barbells left after a fortnight. Everybody wants to make a profit out of you when you have a good Cup run. Nobody wanted to know us a couple of seasons ago when relegation threatened. Now it's different. Of all our players to be taken in it had to be Mac. I'll never forget his face when I leaned out of that window. I could have framed it. What a picture!...

"Whisky Galore"

The arc lights perched on top of the pylons at the corner of Abbey Road training pitch, tried in vain to cast a warm glow onto the murky, misty, November evening. The gathering gloom, however, of that Monday evening in November defied their presence and made the evening no less inviting to the spectators gathered around than to the players in the middle of the field. Perhaps the fact that City had won at Widnes on the previous Sunday had caused a few spectators to leave the warmth of their firesides to stand huddled together, at the side of the players entrance. The ever faithful trio of pensioners in caps and tightly wrapped scarves, for whom a visit to watch City train for an hour meant the cost of a pint of Bitter saved in the local, noted the comings and goings around the training area. A knot of fourteen and fifteen year old girls from the nearby Beaconsfield High School, all giggles, enthused over the latest young recruit from the Colts team and hoped for a glance in their direction. A look from Welsh star Warren Bates would have set their hearts a flutter and brought about an emotional crisis in the classroom. An aged couple passed the group on their way to the Bingo Evening in the club's social lounge, their minds more attuned to "all the fours, forty four" than the numbered shouts on the training area where a pack of 'A' team forwards rehearsed a set move in the corner by the Car Park Entrance. Half a dozen of the 'A' team backs strained and hurtled their way down the cinder track, illuminated by the warm and inviting light of the lounge bar. Each player, conscious that every eye of the spectators was upon them, vied for first place over the short 50 metres sprint. And at the end of their exertions Ken Halsall, the A team coach, checked carefully upon his stopwatch before bellowing out a purely fictitious time - a time arrived at purely to deflate or encourage the winner. Cries of "Never" and "Where did you get that watch from" greeted his announcement of 5.8 secs for the 50 yds. dash.

For the first team squad the evening was a relaxed one after the hard exertions of the previous week which had culminated in the fine win over Widnes. Indeed, Len Topping, allowing his players to unwind before a more strenuous session on the coming Thursday, had not bothered to change into his training gear. Protected from the damp and the cold by his new blue anorak he stood by the side of the social lounge, observing his players indulging in a game of touch rugby.

Training nights after a win at Widnes are to be savoured. There was an air of quiet, calm, satisfaction about Len, all was well with the world. The pressure and stress was off him for the next forty eight hours, at least until Thursday night and the beginning of the build up to the Leeds match. Yet Len knew that deep down the pressures never left him, they only rose or temporarily subsided according to the time of the season. As he cast his eye over the young hopefuls in the Alliance league side and the Colts sprinting before him he pondered in his mind when to start the rebuilding of City's team. He knew that Mac and Tony Smith would have to be replaced, Len Archer on the wing was losing his pace. He needed new blood and the time was rapidly approaching when he would have to employ the surgeon's knife or fireman's hatchet, whichever method he used to rid himself of old favourites. Always a nasty business for a coach to dispense with players who have served him so well, always a gamble when inserting fresh faces into the side, always a risk finding the right blend of personnel! But the job had to be done sooner than later thought Len. But not tonight.

"Just giving them half an hour tonight," Len remarked to Colin Taylor who was standing alongside and who had just parked his Rover 2000 in the Car Park in anticipation of a lengthy Board Meeting over the proposed building of a new social complex. "Can't keep them at peak all the time, you know", Len added, as Colin Taylor nodded, not quite knowing what was peak fitness and what was not. Colin Taylor surveyed the scene but his mind was more concerned with his plans to introduce a new restaurant and social complex at the club as quickly as possible. Indeed the Board Meeting tonight had been convened specially to listen to Colin's plans for the installation of such a complex and the addition of private company sponsorship boxes. He was already late and didn't want to waste any further time watching a nondescript game of touch rugby with Len Topping.

"They deserve it after Sunday's performance. A real team effort was that," replied Colin. He patted Len Topping on the shoulder and left to join the meeting upstairs in the Board Room which had begun a half hour previously. The excited cries from the centre of the pitch - "Offside, Knock on, Forward Pass", indicated that despite Len's relaxing of training there was no casual attitude to the friendly game of touch rugby being played by about twenty of the first team pool of players. The regular weekly game of Forwards versus Backs was in full swing and was being played at a brisk pace despite the catcalls and banter which greeted every try or move from the backs. Most of the caustic comment came from the large shape of Mac whose seventeen stone frame was certainly not lost in the murkiness of the evening. Mac, as ever, was in charge of the forwards and in determined, if joking mood, that none would pass through the ranks of his team to score a try, though he himself seemed to be doing little to stop the opposition. Having taken up his position in the centre of the training pitch he rarely moved his bulk two yards to his left or right and then only to turn to criticise whichever flank had let a try through its ranks. By keeping to the middle he himself could never be blamed and was thus able to give full vein to his comic banter against his own side.

"You're wanted on the telephone, Ken", greeted one slip by Ken Todd, whilst "Hit him with your handbag", urged on Tony Smith, his regular front row partner, to stop a five man overlap of players coming towards him. Like a bandmaster in the park and clad in a bright red tracksuit, on the back of which was emblazoned "Whittle's Pork Butchers", he flapped his arms about, pointing in all directions. On his head he wore a red and white Bob cap, donated by a kind supporter, and tucked down in order to cover his ears. And it needed an extra large Bob cap to cover Mac's ears, the results of many seasons packing down in the scrummage. Such were the growths on either side of his head one could have been forgiven for thinking that the rugby league modelled the handles of the Challenge Cup on Mac's ears. Such was the fearsome aspect of the ears, that 'owd 'Arry used to reckon that if he could stand Mac in the centre of the pitch in August then the crows would bring the grass seed back from July.

"We finely tuned athletes can't risk a cold", was his justification for his training gear. But, on training nights, Mac rarely lingered long enough on the pitch to catch cold, his favourite resting place in November and December being the physiotherapist's table or the warm bath alongside the changing room. Hurling abuse everywhere, he searched in his repertoire for a trick which would give his side a try and one which would give him every justification for calling a halt to the game on the pretext of "last try wins the game" or some other fictitious device for which he was famed. The welcome sight of Sid at the players entrance signalled to Mac that the players' bath was now ready and he for one didn't wish to delay a moment longer. 'Arry by now would be laying his reconditioned soap blocks, one between three if the players were lucky. He had not yet patented a device for fastening the soap to string at the side of the bath but most players considered it only a matter of time before he had perfected the idea, at a further saving to the club's finances. No doubt he would find a sponsor for the string. Sid waved to Len Topping and turned to retreat into the warmth of the club house but not before he had cast a longing look at the knot of Beaconsfield High School girls now grouped around the players entrance. No glances were returned and Sid crept surreptitiously back to his retreat in the skip room, realising that unless he actually donned a red and white hooped jersey of the City team he would always be out of favour.

Mac's mind and eye were also preoccupied with a young lad, aged about twenty two, who had arrived at the ground an hour earlier ready changed in a dark blue tracksuit and training shoes. Stepping quietly into the first team dressing room he had sought Len's permission to train with the club and had enquired as to the possibility of having trials with the 'A' team. Len had eyed him up and down, and noting his strong athletic build, immediately gave him permission, hoping as St. Helens had done years before, to snap up another Cliff Watson, the Great Britain forward who was to emerge from nowhere after such a trial. "If you want a go lad I'll encourage you. Do a few laps and a few sprints. Then have a game of touch rugby with us. I'll see the Board about an 'A' team trial on Friday night." Len didn't press him as to his rugby background, believing that he wished to remain silent through fear of being banned from Rugby Union after a trial with a professional club. However, unable to refrain from being too inquisitive he asked,

"How have you come to the club? Have you run here?" Stan
Pearson, putting a jersey over his head grinned and said,

"What position do you play? Stan looked him over as a potential
threat even though he was the current Great Britain stand off and
had few peers in the game.

"Wing", was the reply and in answer to both questions
added casually,

"My mate dropped me off earlier. He's picking up some cheap
whisky for a couple of licensees in Liverpool. He'll pick me up
after training." The words 'cheap whisky' seemed to float above
all the chatter and noise of the dressing room until they were
picked up by Mac's ears which pricked back like a retriever dog's
in sight of its' quarry. Unlike a retriever dog however, if Mac got
his teeth around a bottle of whisky, no owner would claim his catch.

"What do you mean 'cheap'?" Mac asked.

"Fell off a lorry," beamed the trialist. "A fiver a bottle, though its
mostly for some friends."

"Have you any spare?" asked Stan, thinking of a few cheap
Christmas presents for his friends at work.

"He can possibly spare a hundred bottles but I'll have to limit it to
four or five each."

The lad looked down sheepishly at his rugby boots which he
carried in a large piece of brown paper and proceeded to remove
the dirty blue trainers which he had on his feet. In contrast his
rugby boots were brand new and looked hardly to have been
worn. He placed the boots on his feet but instead of wrapping
the white laces around his instep and ankle for increased support
he tied both at the top in a delicate double knot, rather in the
manner of a ballerina fairy princess.

"Put me down for five," urged Mac. He reached for his trousers hanging from the number ten peg and unbuttoning his back pocket took five crumpled fivers from it and handed them to the trialist.

"I'll need a pencil and paper to remember who wants what," implored the lad. Sid came to the rescue, for having borrowed a fiver from 'Arry he sensed a bargain and, amid delusions of handling illicit Mafia booze, placed his order next to Mac's. An assortment of coins and five pound notes changed hands in a mad scramble to secure a purchase and all craned their necks to see that their names were pencilled on the scrap of paper. With the magical figure of one hundred bottles being reached in quick time the trialist called a halt to the trading.

"Can't promise any more. He might have some extra bottles when he gets back to pick me up, I'll ask him when he comes." The lad, by now growing in confidence, placed all the notes and even the coins in the pockets of his track suit trousers and proceeded to join the rest of the players on the training pitch. Winning money and whisky at a fiver a bottle had made training on that murky November night less demanding than it would have been on a normal evening, whilst the fact that the trialist proceeded to line up in the wing position on Mac's side reassured everyone as to his good intentions. Mac, sensing a regular supply of whisky, looked after the lad and offered him every encouragement during the touch rugby game but, despite his prompting and his constant abuse at his side, no try was forthcoming. In a last desperate bid to close the game, despite the no kicking rule introduced by Mac himself, he placed a grubber kick in the direction of the trialist's wing. The lad, either taken unawares or not knowing what to do, raced in too fast for the ball and, lunging forward, knocked the ball over the line instead of catching it. He was sent sprawling into the perimeter fence.

"Hope you don't drop all that bloody whisky when it comes," joked Stan Pearson from the side. "You've lost Mac. We've won. I'm off for a bath."

Mac grinned and, picking up the lad from the mud by his arm, turned to leave the field whilst the trialist, as if unused to the clinging mud, raised his wet shirt collar from around his neck and adjusted his clinging sleeves at the cuffs.

"Is this your mate?" Mac enquired, as a small blue van turned into the gates, stopped, then moved forward on the edge of the Car Park adjoining the far corner of the training pitch. The headlamps flashed on and off twice in rapid succession as if to indicate to the young trialist that his friend had returned, and with the whisky. Curiously, the driver maintained the engine idling over and made no effort to get out of the van.

"Ask him has he got any more bottles. I'll have another ten bottles if he has any," added Mac.

"I'll ask him," replied the trialist, "But I can't do it for anyone else Mac. Don't tell anyone." He turned towards the blue van in a slow, deliberate manner. He walked on tiptoe threading his way through the mud which had been churned up by the players' exertions. His head turned and with a smile on his face he shouted to Mac, "Do you want anymore if he has any?" Mac nodded vigorously and placed his right forefinger on his lips as if to quieten the lad. If Mac was to get a bargain he wanted to make sure that he was to get an even bigger bargain than the rest of the players. Besides, he thought, there was still a good trade to be had in this whisky at seven pounds a bottle. No sense in flooding the market.

"I'll give you the fifty quid when you come in," shouted Mac. The lad, by now nearing the low railing which surrounded the training

pitch, lifted his right arm casually into the air and, without
turning around, signalled to Mac as if in acknowledgement of his
request. Approaching the perimeter fence he skipped over it with
a nimbleness of foot he hadn't shown in the touch rugby match
and then, curiously, broke into a slow jog as he made his way to
the side of the small blue van.

Mac and the rest of the players trooped slowly from the field,
pausing at the players' entrance to shake off the mud which clung
to their boot studs and track suit bottoms. Stan Pearson stamped
on the asphalt surface with his boots to free his studs of the last
clinging pieces of mud and grass and unzipped his tracksuit
bottoms to shake the dirt from around his ankles. The gloom
finally won its battle as the light from three pylons was switched
off, only the lights at the Car Park corner remaining on until the
players' cars had cleared it later that night. Mac, involved in an
earnest conversation with Tony Smith on the price of whisky at
Barlows Supermarket, was suddenly bathed in light as, on passing
beneath the secretary's office, the window opened wide. The face
of Dick Armstrong, City's long serving secretary, peered out in the
night and, focussing his eyes on Mac, shouted,

"Just had Ted Horrocks on the phone from Oldham. Told me a
trialist did their players for two hundred pounds on Thursday at
training. Supposed to be selling bottles of whisky. Took the
money then buggered off after training. Ted's ringing round to
warn all the Lancashire clubs."

Mac stopped, looked at Tony, his seventeen stones somehow
looming larger as he turned quickly on his heels and back
towards the pitch. And for the first time that night he actually
ran. He ran as fast as he could back to the training pitch, only to
see, too late, the small blue van disappear through the Car Park
entrance. He looked around the deserted training pitch as if for

"We've been bloody done!"

moral support. He was alone. He looked at the car park and the space which the small blue van had once occupied. Everywhere was quiet save for the three pensioners who were in heated conversation as to whether they should repair to the Black Bull where bitter was 1/2d a pint or to the Coach & Horses. Dick Armstrong's face had by now long disappeared from his office window and only the glare of the light from the window bathed the large and angry shape of Mac. Shock, despair and sheer frustration showed on Mac's face. He picked up the nearest and largest clump of mud he could find and, hurling it aimlessly in the air, he seemingly addressed the pitch in a release of his emotion. "We've been bloody done. The bastard! We've been bloody done."

*"So you want a cheque for two hundred and ninety pounds, payable to
Argosy Travel for Len's air fare to Sydney and return. That's not too bad,
John. And you don't want any money yet for that hotel at Coogee Bay. I
see, Len will pay for that himself when he leaves. Fourteen pounds a day
is a fair rate, John. Much appreciated. By Wednesday? Right. I'll let
Len know he'll have the tickets in his hands on Thursday then. His
address? Have I not put it on the form? Hang on a minute, John."*
*Is it 35 or 37? Whoever designed this filing cabinet never kept files in it.
They are always falling off the racks, never in the correct order. I'm sure
somebody goes through these files when I'm not here. For what reason I'll
never know. Here it is - 'Len Topping'.*
*"It's 37 Dalehead Lane, John. Yes, number thirty seven. Okay. Thanks
very much, John. Oh by the way, will you be taking out your usual
perimeter board advertising next season? Good. I'll be in touch. Cheerio."*
*Not a bad price that. Two hundred and ninety pounds return to Sydney.
Saves us some money. Every little penny helps. With these Wembley
receipts, I wouldn't be surprised if Len comes back with a big Aussie prop.
None of these files are in the correct order. Mac's file shouldn't be next to
Len Topping. Just look at Mac's age, thirty five years. No wonder the
Board tried to replace him at the beginning of the season. We must find a
new young prop. Still, Mac had a good season and helped us get to
Wembley, thanks to Bob Royle's problems. Nothing seems to happen
straightforwardly at this club...*

"Gone Scouting"

Bob Royle's visit to the ground of Birkenhead Park Rugby Union Club on that first Saturday in September had been determined not so much by his own inclinations but rather by a chance remark addressed to 'Con' Chapman and himself at one of City's pre-season training evenings. 'Con' and Bob, leaning over the rails surrounding the training pitch, and in their shirt sleeves on that warm evening, had been joined by the vice-chairman, Ben Higson. The sight of Mac, lathered in sweat around his bright red face and having great difficulty in keeping pace with the rest of the track-suited bunch racing around the perimeter of the field prompted Higson to observe, almost to himself.

"We'll have to find somebody to replace Mac. He can't go on forever. We could get a decent price for him in the early season before he is tempted to call it a day. Best beef must be sold before it goes off."

The group's eyes focussed upon Mac who, by now, had stopped at the side of the grass near the players entrance and was in the process of gasping for his breath like some huge Angel Fish which had been taken out of water. Bob, City's chief scout, looked upon Mac with a sympathetic smile and as one who understood that the summer break had indeed taken it's toll upon his body. 'Con' merely noted his lack of physical fitness but Ben Higson's eyes had detected the first signs that their product would soon be at the deterioration stage and that sooner than later would be the time to sell.

"Paintwork looks smart, 'Con'. You've done a good job there. It needed doing though."

Ben switched the conversation, as if deliberately, towards the

newly painted surround and exterior of the club which his firm,
under the watchful eye of 'Con' Chapman had undertaken in the
previous month. The gleaming red and white barriers and the
freshly painted white lettering above the entrances and exits made
a clean background to the recently mown grass area and the
neatly raked cinder track surround. 'Con' cast his eyes around
the full view before giving his considered judgement on the now
completed job but, before he could pass comment, Ben had again
switched the top of conversation back to Mac and asked Bob Royle,
"Have you seen any decent props about on your travels? Not
many good props knocking about these days."
"That young nephew of mine who plays at Birkenhead Park tells
me that there's a good 'un playing against them first match of the
season. Wasps are on tour in the first week. He says that Coulton
their prop is the hardest player he has ever been against. Might
be worth a trip to look at him, Bob. Mr Higson's right. We need
cover for Mac and Tony Smith is no spring chicken you know."
'Con' had forgotten his painting contract, and returned to his
first love, rugby. Bob Royle in reply, nodded slowly and only
raised his head to wink at Len Topping who passed on his way to
coaxing the players around another lap.
Bob had been City's long serving scrum half throughout the
fifties and had figured in the club's championship winning side of
1956/57, only being forced to retire from the league in 1959
when his leg had suffered complications after two operations for
the removal of cartilages. Now a sprightly, dapper, and fit looking
fifty years of age he busied himself during the week, along with
his wife, in the running of the small newsagents shop at the
corner of Abbey Road alongside the ground. Or rather his wife
busied herself in the running of the shop for Bob was usually to
be found slumped over the pile of newspapers near the door,

chatting rugby to City's spectators or selling an endless supply of 'City Pontoon' Lottery tickets to unsuspecting but willing benefactors of the club. Such an efficient business in the hands of a truly devoted wife gave him the time to act as City's chief scout and allowed him to visit many a Union ground where he would quietly merge into the background to watch a possible signing going through his paces. Though his quiet activities were now far removed from his days as a volatile scrum half who had become greatly overheated and prone to stutter in exciting situations on and off the field he nevertheless had had his moments in the scouting field. His white mackintosh had become easily recognisable and, as Bob himself was wont to put it, occasionally, when recognised as a league scout, he had, "been proud to have been thrown out of some of the finest club lounges in the country." Bob had considered for some time that a major overhaul would be needed upon City's forwards but it was not his job to suggest it, only to react when the need for his services was required.

The first Saturday in September invariably bathes the commencement of the Rugby Union season in bright warm sunlight, the warmth of which often tempts the suggestion that God himself is of the true amateur code! Saturday, September 6th was no exception for Bob had been forced to abandon his white mackintosh to the safety of his arm as, almost on the stroke of 3 o'clock, he passed through the small entrance door at the side of the Squash courts at the front of the club. Invariably leaving his entrances to grounds until the last minutes before kick off, once he had adjusted his eyes to the glare of the sunlight which reflected off the white walls of the stand along the near side of the pitch, he was surprised to see a group of casually dressed young men strolling on the pitch whilst the few spectators already in attendance were leaning on the rails with their backs to the pitch. All obviously in no hurry to commence the match. The half dozen players clad in blazers or club sweaters strolled with hands in pockets and occasionally dug their heels into the turf or knelt down to poke a thumb and forefinger into the hard baked soil. All thoughts of summer rugby, often expressed amid the month of January, were furthest from their minds. What few spectators there were, reclined on the rails, consuming the seasons first pint of best Bitter or Lager. A group of three, large, rotund, middle aged gentlemen listened to a young girl, obviously dressed more with an eye for horse riding than rugby, hold forth on the Wine and Cheese Party held at Fiona's on the night previous. All three seemed more interested in her 'body' than that of the wine and cheese. A few had already taken their seats in the long, low and curved stand which ran the full length of the pitch, no doubt eager to seek the freedom of gaining a row rather than a seat to themselves. Having enquired of a small boy, who was dispensing programmes near the gate, as to the reasons for the delay in the kick off Bob was politely but firmly told, "Wasps are arriving late. Held up in traffic on the M6. Old Havertonians are not here yet for the fourth team."

Thus, not wishing to draw too much attention to himself, he looked across at the dirt terracing on the far side of the pitch and, observing only a small cluster of schoolboys grouped around the wooden scoreboard perched at the top of the banking on the half way line, he felt that the bar would be the best place for anonymity until the arrival of the Wasps team. The fact that two or three pints would cool him down also weighed heavily upon his considerations as he made his way towards the old but sedate pavilion which lay at the side of the entrance and at the corner of the field. With its steps leading to the pitch the pavilion seemed designed to disgorge players in white flannels rather than in shorts and jerseys, especially in the sunlight of that Saturday. Nevertheless it provided a welcome retreat for Bob from the glare of the sunlight and the possible over exposure of a Rugby League scout.

Once inside the clubhouse Bob sought the comfort and sanctuary of the small bar and, having watched with pleasure the froth of the Bitter slowly rise to the top of his glass as the bar steward pressed the delivery tap, he raised it to his lips in eager anticipation. He was not disappointed with the local brew and, licking his tongue around his lips, he turned to survey the walls decorated with wooden honours boards on all sides. Bob prided himself on knowing the names and clubs of all the Union converts and, stepping closer to the County and Internationals list he scanned the names looking for Keith Northey, a fine centre who had signed from Birkenhead Park for St. Helens in the early sixties. His search was suddenly interrupted by a tap on his shoulder and, upon turning, his face was confronted by a bunch of lottery tickets, behind which, was the even prettier face of a young girl dressed in a tight fitting white sweater - an obvious sales factor. "Would you like to buy a club lottery ticket? Only 6d a ticket. For the club funds." The lottery ticket seller supreme had been trapped by an amateur, but one with bigger sales aids than Bob could ever muster. He could hardly refuse and, who knows, he might win a fortnight for two in Majorca. Without the wife! It was whilst choosing his ticket from the girl that he first became aware of a pair of eyes fixed in a studied glare upon him, a little further along the bar. Bob looked at the ticket, ripped open the perforated edges and glanced along the bar in the direction of the eyes. The eyes were still fixed upon him. Bob looked at the symbols printed on the lottery ticket - an apple, a cherry, and a

pear. No luck, he had lost. The eyes still followed his every move.
He crumpled the ticket in his hand, and looked for an ashtray on
the bar counter. "Keep calm," Bob thought, "order another
Bitter. Never been thrown out of a Cheshire club house before."
The eyes possessed a small, round, body, dressed in a smart grey
suit, and which now made its way towards Bob, reclining at the
bar and pretending to be so unconcerned.

"No luck? You can't win every time," suggested the stranger. "It's
a mess Wasps being so late. The Old Havertonians were late too,
just arrived. The fourth team will kick off as soon as they can get
ready on the bottom pitch. It will be an hour before Wasps get
here. They've just rung from Knutsford. They're on their way
now. Traffic's been terrible, I believe."

Bob merely nodded and smiled approvingly at this sudden
intrusion upon his quiet drink.

"Yes, it'll be day trippers to Blackpool and The Lakes," he
suggested. "You wouldn't think it was the rugby season with all
this heat." Bob's mind raced as to why the stranger had come
across and already he had visions of him being the club secretary
about to snap his fingers and present two Black Belt, Karate-
punching prop forwards who would deliver Bob swiftly from
the premises.

"I've just moved into the area. Been at Sedgeley Park club in
Manchester. Thought I'd try to get involved with another club
over here," offered Bob, in the hope of placating the gentleman.
He couldn't resist adding, cheekily, "I'm in the removal business."

"Thought I hadn't seen you here before. I watch all the games,"
remarked Bob's newly found friend, as he lifted his gin glass to
his lips.

"I was looking forward to a good game with the Wasps today. Still
a good side. I last watched them when they had Hall and Cooper

playing, before they signed for the rugby league," he continued, looking very closely at Bob.

'He must know,' thought Bob. 'He's testing me. I must get rid of him somehow.'

Bob's eyes swung back along the honours boards and realised that at the end he had spotted the Gents toilets. Relief both physical and mental presented itself to him and, hurriedly making his excuses to the persistent enquirer at his elbow, he darted through the archway and to the safety of the urinal. Precious little safety! "Can you run touch for the Havertonians? One of their cars has broken down. You only need to help until they arrive. You wanted to be involved in a club," beamed the grey suited intruder whose head stretched around the toilet door. Whether from shock and surprise Bob's new suede shoes were immediately showered and, in sheer desperation to rid himself of his hunter, he replied "Yes, if you've got some boots to fit."

Bob had assessed the situation quickly. He must rid himself of his inquisitor or he would give the game away, and also he must relieve himself of his damp shoes. Anyway it would be an hour before the Wasps team arrived. He could watch the main match afterwards. Anything to be rid of his friend from the Gestapo. If there were no boots he could tuck his pants into his socks and hope the suede shoes would dry in the sun. Anything to get out of the clubhouse.

'He must know,' thought Bob.

"They'll be here in twenty minutes," the captain of the Old Havertonians reassured Bob as they walked down the steps and along the touchline of the first team pitch. Bob, though looking like an ancient British Rail guard, holding the red flag in his hand, walked alongside the players and wondered how the hell a League scout came to be running the touchline for a Union club.

He was only too pleased however to be free of the 'scoutcatcher' who remained at the top of the club steps, his gin glass still firmly gripped in his hand. Bob and the players had hardly gone twenty yards along the front of the main stand on their way to the second pitch behind the cinder terracing at the far end of the ground when he froze. Before his eyes, seated in the front row of the Grandstand was a fate worse than his previous interrogation. He had caught sight of the familiar round shape of Ken Ackers, the aged Oldham scout, who was sat huddled over the match programme. If Ken, who had spent so many years scouting that it was even rumoured that he approached Adam before Eve and had offered a far better deal than an apple, had spotted Bob a torrent of ridicule would have ensued from his lips.

"Bloody 'ell Ken Ackers. The bloody shame of it. He'll tell everybody I'm running the touchline for a rugby union club. I'll never live it down. How can I get past him without him seeing me?" thought Bob. "If this gets out I'm finished. I'll end up scouting for Baden Powell!" He turned his back on the stand and Ken Ackers, and proceeded to shuffle sideways whilst continuing a conversation with two large front row forwards in the hope that he would not be spotted by his arch rival for signatures. His dodge, or to be more precise, his shuffle, had worked for he was soon past the stand and onto the far pitch for that rare experience in his rugby career, touch judge for a union club. The first twenty minutes of his new career had been spent in a frustratingly endless stream of mistakes which had been brought about by his not realising the difference between League and Union in regard to the kicking of the ball out of play without a bounce. Fostered on a staple league diet which had trained Bob that all kicks to touch had to bounce before crossing the line he could make little headway under the Union ruling whereby the ball must bounce between the twenty two metres lines, but need not from a kick inside of them. Thus he continually found himself in conflict with the small moustached generalissimo in midfield who masqueraded under the title of a referee and whose sole delight lay in performing a concerto with his whistle and barking orders all around.

'Obviously a refugee from his wife's kitchen,' thought Bob, as he grew more hot under the collar after a slight altercation with both the referee and the home fullback following one disputed good touch kick.

"Keep your eyes on the ball. You shouldn't be running touch if you don't know the laws," snapped the little dictator, as with a flick of his finger he pointed to the exact spot upon which he expected Bob to stand.

"And put your flag up more quickly," he commanded, before turning his back upon him to observe the formation of the lineout. 'I bloody know I shouldn't be running touch,' mused Bob as he fought to control his anger at what he considered to be his public humiliation. 'It's not the ball my eyes should be concentrating on, it's the Wasps front row.'

With the conclusion of the lineout and the transfer of play to the other side of the pitch Bob pondered over his ridiculous situation as he gently rubbed the underside of his chin with his flag stick. His mind tangled with the complexities of explaining to City's directors his inability to observe the Wasps' front row. He daren't tell them the full story. He would have to make up a very non-committal report on the player and ask for a second opinion from a director. He'd say Coulton hardly touched the ball, was hardly in the game, anything to hide his embarrassment. He wasn't bothered. After all, it was Bob who had signed Don Thompson the club's goalkicking record holder from Waterloo in 1963 even

*"Unfortunately Bob was
underneath him but with his
flag still held aloft"*

though, on only his second trip, he failed to find the ground. A good report in the Liverpool Echo over four pints of Bitter in the Stanley Arms had convinced Bob of his abilities for league!

"Do you mind. We're trying to play a game here." The shrieking snarl of the little referee rudely awoke Bob to the fact that he was still rooted to the halfway spot whilst play had actually been taken to within five yards of the Old Havertonians try line via a good kick from the Birkenhead Park team's fullback.

"Oh sorry," replied Bob, resisting the urge to hit the referee with the flag stick. "I wasn't with it."

"You won't be with us much longer if you carry on like this. I'm used to better officials than this with the Liverpool referees society," snapped the apprentice Hitler, obviously relishing his delusions of starting play in some crucial British Lions match of the future. Bob, feeling the frustration of the curtailed scouting mission and his anger rising up within him, raised his flag aloft and strode quickly to the required spot.

"Here, not there," insisted Hitler, making Bob move to his left at least three inches. With play about to commence and with the referee having taken up a position at the back of the lineout, the ball immediately rebounded off the prop's head back into Bob's direction. Bob, forgetting his role of touch judge and thoroughly confused by the implications of his job, grabbed the ball as it hovered almost on the touch line in front of him. Disaster arose in the shape of an attacking winger, a young pimple-faced youth of tremendous exuberance who, making the same instinctive reaction, grabbed at the ball which hung in front of Bob. A clash of arms, a trip from a defending prop, a push from the hooker, and the wing was over the line for a disputed try. Unfortunately Bob was underneath him but with his flag still held aloft from his arm which jutted out of the melee which had formed on top of him.

"Try, ref, try!"

"Rubbish. In touch."

"A yard in touch."

Abuse and comment filled the air around Bob who, by now thoroughly fed up and angered, pushed bodies away from himself. "Well?" The referee looked at Bob for guidance and poked his little face above Bob's as he struggled to his feet. Still feeling the impact of the winger's shoulder in his stomach Bob gulped for breath and, pursing his lips, his stutter robbed him of any speech. Only a series of incoherent sounds greeted the referee's inquiry. He fought for his words but none would come, only empty mouthings in the face of the exasperated referee who was now being accosted by both sets of players as to a decision.

"Don't take the piss out of me, touch judge. I've had enough. Get off. I'll do the touch myself. No try!" And off the referee ran to the twenty two metres line for the drop out, definitely relishing his firm decision which would no doubt, in his mind, reverberate through every clubhouse in the North. He would make sure of that.

It would certainly reverberate through every League club if anyone found out Bob's predicament. He had regained his speech control sufficiently to mutter aloud, "Didn't want to do it in the first place. Only helping them out."

Throwing the red flag to the ground he abandoned his post and began the silent trudge back to the first fifteen match, now in progress on the adjoining pitch. He was almost glad to have been sent off and content with the thought that at least he could watch the player he had come to see without further disturbance. He loosened his trouser bottoms from his stockings as if to give him anonymity when he emerged from behind the terracing and onto the surround of the main pitch. He combed his hair and straightened his tie more tightly around his collar.

'Nobody will ever know.'

He moved to the rails. And yet he still didn't feel comfortable. He sensed eyes behind him.

"Pst! Pst!" Bob turned sharply to see the face of Ken Ackers, leaning out of the front row of the grandstand, a wide grin on his face, his programme held to the side of his mouth in a mocking gesture to muffle his words.

"Fancy a trial as a touch judge with Oldham? Good expenses. You can have your flag. We're on the look out for good young talent, Bob. I'd have to come and watch you first though."

Not again! There's no rest even in the summer. "Hello. No, I'm afraid the Board of Directors haven't come to a decision yet. Yes, I can appreciate that. You need at least three weeks before the season starts to install the wires underground. There's a full Board meeting on July 10th when the cost of installing underground heating is on the agenda. If they decide to go ahead with the project that should give you enough time to work on the pitch. Can you ring back after that date then? Okay, I'll hear from you then. Bye."

It's time the Directors made their minds up on this underground heating matter. You'd think Ben Higson had the grass laid down in his lounge the way he goes on about protecting the turf. When will he ever learn that you don't have to dig up the ground? We need more clubs with underground heating after our experience in the Semi Final. Moving that match to the Wednesday night because of frost probably cost us around five thousand pounds. More work for the secretary too. Players didn't mind as long as the match didn't interfere with their outing on the Thursday. No chance of that happening after the result...

"All Steamed Up!"

'The morning after the night before' failed to register the usual meaning for Mac, resting his seventeen stones on the front seat of the coach, a case of beer at his feet, and with the newspaper alongside him. For Mac's "morning after" there were bottles of beer in abundance and, as yet, a clear head to face the day's outing along with the rest of the City players to Southport Municipal Golf Course. Nothing could dampen the enthusiasm and delight at the dramatic last minute win on "the night before" at St. Helens in the Semi Final of the Challenge Cup for, as the coach sped along the Rainford By Pass towards Burscough, all the players were engrossed in the wide variety of Thursday's daily papers. All eagerly scanned the columns in the back pages for the merest mention of their names, yet all were content to bask in the glory being heaped on the team as a whole in their last minute surge to victory. Brian Batty of the Mail had dubbed the game "Warren's last gasp" whilst Alan Thomas had been more forthright in the Express which blared forth with "Floodlight Robbery". "Last Gasp" or "Robbery" would worry few of the players, facing the prospect of a relaxing day's golf at Southport to be followed by a steak dinner on the way home - the results of Mac's weekly collection of one pound per week from their pay packets during the season. The fact that a further £70 per man had been added to their funds, following last night's win, further fostered their contentment.

"Planned rugby, that's what it was," beamed Stan Pearson, sitting midway down the coach and studying the report as he leaned forward in the aisle to open another bottle of Light Ale from one of the many boxes dotted about the coach on empty seats. Stan,

resplendent in his black club blazer and grey slacks, would have
passed for an Insurance Agent rather than the welder who was
accustomed to arriving at training in his grease-stained boiler suit,
his change of clothes wrapped in a brown paper parcel ready for
after his shower.

"Planned rugby, eh, Warren?" he grinned and smiled in the
direction of Warren Bates, the ex Welsh Rugby Union star, who, as
the principal figure of the previous night's drama could think of
little planning to the last few minutes of the match.

"Chaos," thought Warren, as his mind floated back to the final
two minutes of the drama which had begun when he had elected
to kick at goal, with City trailing by 13 points to 7 points. The
kick had been an easy one in front of the posts but had been
greeted with derision by the City supporters who had wished the
players to take a tap penalty and go for a try. Though the frantic
crowd had forgotten the necessity of two scores being required to
erase Wigan's six point lead, Warren, never turning aside gift
points, duly slotted the ball between the posts to reduce the
deficit to four points.

Those spectators who had left the ground early, vowing never to
return again, now charged back onto the terraces for the last kick
off. But a careful check from at least 20,000 watches had surely
revealed that, with only one minute remaining, Wigan still had a
firm grip on the game. Particularly as the entire Wigan side
dawdled back to the centre line in an effort to waste those
precious seconds before the sound of the final whistle. Yet, after
only one tackle, made on Todd, from the kick off, young Frank
Scahill, after a couple of appearances on the substitutes bench,
and now playing in his first senior game, took the Wigan defence
by surprise. Taking up his position for Todd to play the ball back
to him, he darted clear, left the Wigan player opposite him

clutching air and sped towards the Wigan try line. With the Wigan defence pierced, and furiously attempting to cover back, the City back line swept upfield to run onto Frank's neatly timed pass. The ball was transferred at pace along the line towards the right wing where Warren Bates had the easiest of runs from twenty yards out, to place the ball near the corner flag. Unable to race around in order to put the ball between the posts, thanks to the skillful covering of the Wigan full back, he had settled for a safe try but at the risk of an unsure conversion from the touchline. The fairy tale ending had taken the crowd by surprise as one section waited for the ensuing kick with baited breath while the other half whistled and jeered in an attempt to unnerve the kicker. But Warren, who with one successful conversion would help to repay half of his £15,000 signing on fee of earlier in the year, had struck the ball crisply with his left foot. He had no need to raise his head to follow its flight. He knew, instinctively, that it would pass over the cross bar and between the posts.

"Some bloody planning," laughed Warren. "Don't give me any more of those to kick. My heart will never stand the strain. My hands are still shaking now, I'll never hold the putter today. Bear in mind, a hockey stick will be good enough for Mac and Sid. "What do you think, Stan?" "Don't know," replied Stan, who had been drawn, along with Warren, to play against Mac and Sid, the worst golfers in the history of Rugby League.

The players waited for a quick retort from Mac. But Mac was not to be drawn at this stage of the day, being too intent upon opening for himself a further bottle from the case. He held the bottle at arms length so as not to shower his new sweater with the froth. Under the new light blue, tight-fitting sweater and, exaggerated by his latest Marks & Spencer's close fitting check trousers, his belly protruded to such an extent that many a

passing observer would have been justified in placing a tap on it
as if to catch the beer at source.

"We'll see, eh, Sid," was all he would offer. "You've not seen us
play golf yet Stan. No taff from the Welsh valleys will beat us Sid."
He gave a knowing wink at Sid, seated behind him, "We'll show
'em for dragging us here!" Though happy to travel to John
O'Groats if there was ale on the coach, Mac and Sid had been
heavily outvoted in the discussions as to where the players should
go for their outing. Mac's suggestion of a trip to York races,
followed by a visit to a strip club in Leeds on the way home had
received only one additional vote - that of Sid whose lifelong
interest in the two legged variety of fillies had outweighed all his
other considerations.

"We'll make you pay for dragging us to a bloody golf course,"
moaned Mac as he turned to wipe dry a speck of foam which had
eluded him and had fallen onto the sleeve of his sweater.

The remainder of the players however were looking forward to a
leisurely stroll around the greens in a not too serious knockabout
and were basking in shirt sleeves in the sun surprisingly streaming
through the coach windows. City's answer to Jack Nicklaus and
Arnie Palmer however remained unmoved and, in a relaxed
mood, both applied their thoughts elsewhere as the coach passed
the clock tower in the centre of Ormskirk. Mac still had three
winners to select from the races at York for his 'three doubles and
a treble' bet and was engrossed in the racing pages of the Daily
Express. Sid had nestled down in his seat for a keen study of a
copy of the girlie magazine which he had found on the floor -
obviously dropped by some frustrated schoolboy on the coach's
schools run earlier that morning.

Nevertheless, by the time the coach driver had dropped the party
on the pavement at the seafront Municipal Course, having had his

instructions to return at 4pm, Mac and Sid were in fine form verbally for the ensuing contest with Stan Pearson and Warren Bates.

"No contest this," intimated Mac, as he wheeled his golf clubs along the pathway with all the air of an experienced golfer, indeed one who had done a 69 on the Crazy Golf at Butlins. Sid, who to date had failed to win a big championship at Butlins and had only his form on the Salford Parks Pitch and Putt to rely upon, declared that he would rely on "his big match experience" as well as an ice cream cornet hastily purchased at the kiosk nearby. Stan and Warren, both good golfers, settled down for a few laughs amid a relaxing day after what had been for Warren the most hectic season of his career. The fact that Warren was down to play a foursome with the club's two most celebrated comics, Mac and Sid, and alongside city's most experienced player in Stan Pearson indicated the acceptance of Warren amongst the players and staff and was an insight into the depth of respect towards him at the close of his first season in the game. Following his initial impact upon the game, during which time the mere lacing up of his boots was enough to merit Warren two inches of newspaper column, his game had deteriorated to such an extent that he had begun to doubt the wisdom of his conversion to League. He had failed to realise the time needed to adjust to the different style of the game and had been so naive in his approach on the field that many centres could take advantage of him. But such had been his determination, and that of Maureen, his wife, that he had ploughed on through his bad patch until the ball had begun to bounce his way again. Success on the field had given him respect off it, not only from the spectators but most important from the players who could sense a player with pride in his profession and with the will to succeed.

"Tha's got to admire a trier," was Mac's comment. A comment
which could equally be applied to Mac himself as he and Sid
strode to the first tee to do battle over eighteen holes. Well,
three! The finely cut turf, the well raked sand in the bunkers,
and the crisply laundered flags at the holes didn't exactly inspire
Mac and Sid to great golf, rather the reverse. "Murder at No. 1
Tee" proved an apt description for, with a lofty strike high into the
air, Mac proceeded to hit a pigeon, calmly flying above, which
came down with a thud fifty yards ahead of him. Since dead
pigeons are not exactly catered for in the rules of golf, after much
discussion and argument, it was agreed that Mac be allowed to
throw his ball onto the green. A lusty throw had in fact
overstepped the green and caused the ball to roll into a bunker
from which, after three strikes at the ball, a further throw to the
pin was conceded by Warren and Stan. Meanwhile, Sid, aided by
a few clean strikes and a couple of kicks at the ball, when Mac was
diverting attention, had managed to hole in Nine. With two
further putts Mac had achieved the remarkable score of eight,
recorded as 3 throws, 3 shots and 2 kicks at the ball! Hardly
championship golf.

Their efforts proved a disaster and, after much good humour,
both declared their withdrawal from the game after a torrid third
hole during which Sid had hit Mac on the back of the head with
his club and lost his sole ball in the rough. Mac retired from the
game with a typical comment of "who picked this bloody partner
for me?" and sought refuge in the tea bar at the clubhouse where
Sid, having informed Warren to have the coach pick them up at
the Boating Lake at quarter past four, joined him. Amid a
discussion as to where the pair should spend the next few hours
Sid cast regular glances at the girl behind the tea bar, a girl who
would surely have been refunded her money on the Ghost Train,

but to Sid, "Beauty was in the eye of the Beholder", especially when there was a chance of developments. Mac however soon put a stop to his desires when, with a sweep of his hand he knocked both plastic cups from the metal table into the nearby waste bin and declared, "The Baths - we'll have a dip. Be good for the bruises Sid. There's an indoor pool on the promenade. Come on. Forget her Sid. You know what they say Sid? When you're young you play football and Rugby, but when you get older you play golf. Which only goes to prove that the older a Sportsman gets the smaller his balls go!" Sid, though resenting the remarks as to his age, acquiesced with a smile and, consoling his desire behind the tea bar with a seductive wink, followed Mac through the doors and out towards the Baths.

"Much more relaxing than swimming all those lengths. Just what we needed, Sid." Mac spoke out of the corner of his mouth as, reclining on the wooden bench fixed to the white tiled wall of the Turkish Baths, he peered through the swirling steam at the back pages of his newspaper. His eyes straining at the lists of horses declared runners for the day. He lay on the white towel, stamped Municipal Baths, which covered the bench and, surrounded by forwards Tony Smith and Ken Todd who had also decided to join them at the expense of the golf, resembled the living Buddha. "Cavalry Charge in the 4.15pm at Kempton Park should give Pat Eddery a hat trick," was all that was forthcoming. There would be no inspirational moral pronouncement from this Buddha today! The decision to visit the Turkish Baths had been taken by Mac, as usual, who insisted that he was too tired to race Sid up and down any swimming pool. He had observed that it would be more relaxing and that he could take a little weight off at the same time, not forgetting to assert that it would "clean Sid's pores out". The four however looked to be most unlikely visitors sitting around on the benches amidst the portly and flabby shapes of assorted business men engaged in the Guardian crossword or their weekly novel from the local library. The usual occupants, refugees from the outside world of Black Forest Gateaux and French Fries, watched with interest as Sid wandered around the room, his eight stones frame encircled by the white bath towel which was handed to all entrants. Like a ghost peering through the mists Sid poked about the large room and made his way to a small wooden door at the corner into which he peeped curiously. "Looks like a toilet," he observed.

"Watch you don't fall down," remarked Tony.

"If you sweat any more they'll think you are the chain," snapped Mac alluding sarcastically to Sid's eight stone frame.

A balding man, whose face suggested that he had fled inside to escape disaster on the Stock Markets, slowly pointed out that, "It's the Hot Room for taking off a few of those unwanted extra pounds, quickly. You must stay in for a few minutes only though. It can do you harm."

Mac stirred on his bench, raised himself upright, and finding no pocket on his nude body in which to place his folded copy of the newspaper, placed it on the bench behind him. He slowly crossed to the wooden booth.

"You sit on the seat inside and close the door. You'll sweat more than in here. You're supposed to put your feet in a bucket of cold water. It's supposed to balance some mechanism in your head, I think. Stops you from getting too weak by sweating too much." The balding man delivered his knowledge in a low voice showing little emotion.

"Have a go Mac, get that spare tyre off quickly," beamed Sid.

"Can't see a bowl in here," replied Mac as he rooted around in the bare wooden cubicle which revealed a solitary wooden seat attached to the back.

"You won't need a bowl, Mac, you've no mechanism in your head," joked Ken.

Ignoring the sarcasm, Mac ascended the wooden seat with the calm deliberation of an Indian Rajah about to have his weight assessed in diamonds, adjusted the white bath towel around his waist, and sat down.

"Shut the door Sid, I'll give it three minutes. I'll bang on the door when I want to come out." With a glint in his eye Sid nodded, shut the door and, turning to Ken, whispered, "We'll fry the swine. He'll come out like a bloody chip!" All three leaned heavily on the brown door and, after three minutes, despite bangs and pushes from within, they never budged.

"Open up, open up, I'm dying in here," screeched Mac. But only guffaws of delight could be heard outside the door as all conjured up visions of Mac being reduced to the proverbial boiled lobster. Suddenly a silence fell upon the cubicle. The banging on the inside of the door ceased, the exertions behind stopped, and only the heavy thud of a body hitting against the inside of the door could be heard.

"He's fainted. Get him out, quick," urged Ken.

"He's faking, he's having us on," insisted Sid.

"He had no bucket of water for his feet," moaned Dr. Gloom who had abandoned his library book to watch the entire proceedings with an air of disdain.

Mac was indeed sprawled out. Half slumped forward from his seat, his head resting against the inside of the door. As the door opened outward he fell forward onto the stone floor, seemingly out for the count.

"Hell, he's bad," insisted Tony.

"Is he hell," remarked Sid, laughing aloud and only appreciating

"As the door opened, he fell forward onto the stone floor, seemingly out for the count."

the funny side.

"It could affect his heart," offered the bald man who by now would only be satisfied with a spectacular death for his admission money.

Mac stirred slowly as Sid and Tony, still laughing and appreciating no serious circumstances, turned him onto his back on the stone floor. Other circumstances were only appreciated however when the attendant, on hearing the commotion and laughter in the room, poked his head around the door. He gulped and bawled in a high pitched voice,

"Get him upstairs, quickly, onto a bed. Bloody fools!"

In his white coat, three sizes too big for him, he raced into the room shod in a pair of plastic slippers obviously designed for such emergency rescues. Being used to greater days as a Staff Sergeant in World War Two he took up his position a couple of yards away from the group, pointed his arm in the direction of the door and barked his orders.

"Careful. Lift him gently. Carry him upstairs. Let him have a rest on one of the beds. He's overdone it. It's weakness."

Offering no physical help, he caught sight of the bald gentleman, watching over the operations avidly, and raised his eyebrows aloft as a sign of his despair and exasperation at the trio attempting to raise Mac from the floor. Mac's bulk did indeed need considerable expertise and exertion on their part.

"I know now how that Captain Ahab must have felt when he harpooned Moby Dick," joked Sid, grappling with two huge trunks which passed for Mac's legs and which were wrapped around his waist and held not too securely at the knees.

"Don't drop his head Tony, you'll crack the floor."

With arms and legs flailing and flapping around, Moby Dick, with one eye open and now observing the action, was transported up the stairs behind the attendant who led the way. The prize catch was placed on a bed, covered with a thin sheet and ordered to rest for half an hour, during which time he was instructed to sip a cup of hot tea which had been placed at his side.

Despite the concern of the little moustached attendant who had seized his chance to launch into a lecture on the dangers of dehydration of the body, and who had probably seen little action since his stretcher bearing days of the Blitz, the players could only laugh at Mac's predicament. Mac, though feeling weak, felt inclined to exaggerate his condition and thus prepared himself mentally to endure the cynical comments hurled in his direction. "See if his balls are still there," quipped Sid. "They reckon they dry up like prunes."

Mac couldn't resist, "Yours will disappear when I get off here Sid. They'll be on the end of bloody cocktail sticks when I've finished with you."

"I'll bet you've lost weight, Mac," sympathised Ken Todd.

"Two stones," chortled Sid.

"I feel as if I'm floating. I'll need lead weights in my boots to keep me down. I'll use Sid's head," Mac added as an afterthought. He lay still and huge beneath the thin sheet, only his feet sticking out at the end of the bed, his toes curled and gnarled, the victim of many stampings in the front row of the scrum. Sid, fearing for his safety and attempting to soothe the white whale now beginning to stir and thrash about verbally on the bed, beat a hasty retreat on the pretext of bringing the coach from the Boating Lake down to the Baths.

"It'll save you all the trouble of walking, Mac. Mustn't exert yourself too early you know."

"He'll be okay now," added the attendant. His lecture now over and the drama having subsided, he no longer desired to be bothered with Mac, especially now that the half past four tea break was being signalled.

"Keep an eye on him. He'll soon be back to normal."

With such encouraging words ringing in his ears Mac raised himself from the bed, reached for his clothes which lay on a chair at the side and slowly proceeded to dress. Leaving his shoes until the last he tied his laces as he sat upright on the side of the bed. Still a little unsteady on his feet, he made his way along the row of six beds, past the tea urn perched precariously on a trolley near the doorway, through the foyer and out onto the pavement where the coach had drawn up alongside. Sid had positioned himself at the corner of the back seat as far away as possible and thrust a wide grin at the window. Tony and Ken had followed Mac on his unsteady course, keeping their distance like bridesmaids, saying little and suppressing their laughter at every exaggerated movement of his legs and body.

Mac greeted the ribald comment and laughter which heralded his arrival on the coach with, "Could have died in there today. My mind will probably be scarred for life." He added, "You find out your friends," and, casting his eye around for Sid, cowering down on the back seat, his face broke into a sly grin. He took his accustomed seat at the front of the coach, reclined his head in the padded rest behind, closed his eyes and stretched his legs fully out into the aisle alongside the driver.

"I feel like a balloon, I could take off from the floor."

Opening his eyes he turned his head slightly backwards in the direction of Stan Pearson sitting behind.

"Need something inside me, Stan, to hold me down. Some ballast. We'll stop at Ormskirk. Thursday's market day there. The pubs are open all afternoon, I think I could just go half a dozen draught Guinness!"

Yes, Mac was 'okay'. He was getting back to normal even quicker than the attendant could have anticipated. He would soon be on the road to a full recovery.

That programme will be worth a few bob in a few years time, all those autographs. I'll keep that in the drawer. No wonder Warrington were favourites with those names - Parkin, Canning, Scott, Marsden - it was some game. It was all worth it if only to see the faces of the Cartwrights on the bus. Like little boys they were. And it wasn't only at the thought of the Wembley receipts too. The cheque was certainly handy, I'll admit. I'll pay this buffet bill. It'll stop Alice pestering about the office. She certainly made a good job for the lads. Nearly cost the club a sponsor though...

"Celebrations"

The sight of a mushroom vol ou vent, delicately balanced between the thumb and forefinger of Mac's huge fist, brought a wry smile to the face of Len Topping. Particularly when he noticed the grace of the crooked little finger. Such a vision was reserved for few rugby league coaches, the sight of a huge fist wrapped around the oval ball or a pint of draught ale being more the order of Mac's day. Observing Mac's attempts at social grace made Len self conscious of the paper plate nestling on the palm of his hand and, placing it on the edge of the buffet table, he casually nibbled at its contents - half a meat pie, a sausage roll, two ham sandwiches and a stick of celery - all served by Alice, the club's help, and her three daughters.

"We must have made some money for the club on Saturday if even the Bingo's been cancelled," Len dryly remarked to Mac who had moved alongside.

"Aye, first Monday I've ever seen with no number being called. You can even talk tonight," replied Mac.

The team indeed earned some money for the club, whilst all the talk on that Monday night among the guests in City's social lounge centred around their appearance at Wembley on the previous Saturday. Gate receipts of over eight hundred thousand pounds had put plenty of money in the players' pockets and especially in the club's coffers. To such an extent that no expense had been spared for the 'Thank You' buffet for the players and club staff. As Mac, Len and Con Chapman gathered at the end of the buffet table which ran the length of one side of the social club, all three appreciated the hard work and efforts of Alice who scurried to and fro behind the white topped trestle tables urging her daughters to attend to her heroes, the players.

Alice, the club washerwoman, having no sons, looked upon the players as her own and certainly made sure they were all well fed in the tea room after matches. However, tonight she had excelled herself with her tables bulging with food fit for her gods, or at least her players. Meat pies, sausage rolls, meat pies, ham sandwiches and more meat pies formed large castles at intervals along the tables, only punctuated by jars of celery sticks and trays of lettuce and tomato. All lovingly purchased that afternoon by Alice herself at the local market.

"No expense spared," said Alice. "Tomatoes were 2/6d a pound you know." Her daughters displayed their care for the players, staff and guests by continually forcing plates of food upon unsuspecting gourmets crowded around the tables. Her youngest daughter Mary displayed her own wares to any player who cared to notice the low cut dress which was frequently offered before their eyes. Holding her serving plate outstretched she leaned forward to Con Chapman and inquired if he might care to try anything. Con, stooping more than usual, as he focussed his eyes on the cleavage, steadied himself with a gulp of his customary whisky, and, as if in apologetic tone suggested,

"No thanks, I've had enough."

"Wonder how much a pound those are, Len?" suggested Mac as he reached for a ripe tomato from Mary's plate.

"I'll bet they took some horse manure, eh Len," he added with a wicked wink of the eye after a sharp glance at Mary's abundant charms. Len failed to reply but managed a half grin with the side of his mouth, the other half being occupied in chewing the remains of a celery stick. His mind too was occupied and reflecting over the journey from the station that night through the red and white bedecked streets to the City club, their reward for that 18 points to 7 victory over Warrington.

The older players had appeared more excited than anyone at
enjoying and relishing a possible last fling and had eagerly sought
their places around the top of the open roofed coach which was
to carry them from the station to the club. Mac, holding the cup
aloft at the front of the coach, was rumoured to have had his
hands welded to the handles immediately on leaving the playing
area at Wembley. Certainly no player could recall the occasion
that weekend when Mac's face had not appeared beneath, around
or on top of the cup. But few begrudged his elation, at thirty six
years of age he was unlikely to appear at the stadium again in any
playing capacity. Stan Pearson, of whom it was also rumoured
that the Queen had handed him a bottle of Newcastle Brown Ale
instead of the customary winners medal, balanced precariously at
the back of the open space with his feet dangling inches above
the head of a very nervous Mr. Benjamin Higson. Ben feared not
only Stan's imminent fall but also the ominous thud of a cluster
of bottles of Newcastle Brown Ale held in Stan's hand. As the
crowds had surged alongside, the coach had been forced into
sudden halts. So to, did Stan sway too and fro but not once did
he stumble over his lines,

"Oh where did she get that hat......" which, though he roared at
the top of his voice, was unheard amidst the deafening roars of
the densely packed crowds below. The adulation of the crowds,
their incessant chants of "City, City", interspersed with roars of
"We've won the Cup" had it's effect too on the directors who
beamed huge smiles through the coach windows. The sort of
smiles usually reserved for victorious politicians who have seen
their policies vindicated with the right result on the day. The
correct buying and selling had been done throughout the season
and this too was their victory. None celebrated more than the two

*"Mac was rumoured to have had his
hands welded to the handles immediately
on leaving the playing area at Wembley"*

Cartwright brothers, Sam and Charles, who had both cast aside their cloak of respectability. Not solicitors today, but young fans in their red and white scarves, their red and white Bob caps, and their huge red and white rosettes pinned to their waistcoats. Both vied for space at the window in order to grin, wave, gesticulate and offer any gesture to the fans lined along the pavements. Had not Sam scored the winning try in his own mind? Had not Charles deluded himself into thinking that he had given the vital defence splitting pass? Few would begrudge two seventy years old schoolboys reliving their dreams in that coach on the way to the ground. Their only return to reality was Sam's constant cry to the top of the coach where he continually reminded Warren Bates, "Watch the angel on the top of the cup. Saints broke it off in '61. Had to be repaired you know, Warren. Better leave the lid off." Len Topping had viewed the homecoming welcome from the corner seat at the rear of the coach, forcing himself to smile, wave and appear elated. After the tension and build up of the previous week he felt drained of all emotion and, leaning his head against the juddering window, he longed for one of Alice's cups of sweet tea which he knew would await their arrival at the City ground. His nerves had calmed and a sense of quiet satisfaction had settled upon him, an emotion far removed from his experiences sat on the trainer's bench that Saturday. Only Len could explain his strained condition whilst watching City's backs probe for that defensive opening in the second half. The forward probes of Harrison and Todd had gone close but midway through the half he had known that with the score at seven points to six points in Warrington's favour the result was in the balance. Only a supreme effort or an extraordinary piece of luck would take City and Len to victory. A combination of both arose out of a very ordinary scrum beneath the Warrington posts at which both sets of props grappled and mauled at each other, causing the scrum to sway around. With Mac insistent upon staying upright at open side prop, in order to give Tom Harvey, the hooker, a better sight of the ball, and with Tom himself swinging low in the scrum the end product was a shambles. Who would win? Mac and Tom Harvey or Sid Abram the referee? Mick Harrison paid little concern to the battle of wits up front as, at loose forward, he stood up from the scrum and surveyed the field for an opening. Frank Scahill walked behind Mick, whispered the command, and Len could only sweat on the crowded bench not knowing that the play had been set. Parkin, the Warrington scrum half, sensing that the referee was rapidly losing his patience and ever aware that the televised cameras were relaying the match to millions, suddenly picked up the ball from his side of the scrum. With an upward flick of the ball he attempted to find a gap down the middle of the tunnel which was blocked by a mass of contorted and writhing arms and legs. A veritable Dante's inferno. The ball failed to find a gap but was splayed back from the side of Mac's bottom and, upon Sid Abram's command of "Play on", it was snapped up by the irrepressible Frank Scahill. Amid screams and shouts of abuse from Canning, the Warrington prop, accompanied by a query as to the nature of the referee's birth from their hooker lying in a crumpled heap on the floor, Frank scampered away. Slipping a ball inside to Mick Harrison, who broke quickly and kept close to the scrum, he had made the perfect opening dreamed of by all loose forwards when five yards from the opposition line.

"You could have driven a bus through," Mick later observed. The try had been a formality, the Warrington hooker had duly been warned as to his behaviour, and Warren Bates had easily put over the conversion to place City well on the path to victory.

To Len Topping it had been the fruition of a years work. All those nights of training in the mud and rain at Abbey Road had been worthwhile. The sight of that try would be etched in his memory for seasons to come. It was certainly etched in his memory more clearly than that of Stan Pearson who now made his way towards the group in the social club, wobbling on his feet, and attempting to steady a double whisky which was slopping over the glass in his hand. Whisky and Newcastle Brown Ale were hardly conducive to preserving stability, and both had left their effects on Stan who beamed a huge smile across his face in greetings to Mac and Len.

"Bloody hot in here, isn't it?"

The perspiration on Stan's forehead and the sweat beneath the arms of his open necked shirt indicated the truth of his remark. His club blazer and tie had been left in the safe custody of Doreen his wife who had retired gracefully from the function to put the kids to bed.

"We did 'em Len," observed Stan as he placed his arm around Len's shoulder and propelled his nose to within a half inch of Len's. "We did 'em. We stuffed 'em, Len."

"We sure did," replied Len in softer tones, as if attempting to soothe and quieten Stan in the hope that he might restrain himself from making a scene, especially with such dignitaries around. Hoping to engage Stan in a quieter discussion Len naively offered,

"Had a good weekend Stan?"

Stan, in the act of tipping a further whisky into his glass, shuffled on his feet with all the artistry of a master stand off but he was in little condition to execute his famed sidestep.

"Did you see the tits on Mary, tonight, Len," was Stan's only reply. Len nodded as if registering his approval of the fact that Mary 'had them on every night' but couldn't resist a coach's customary caution.

"You'll never keep fit off whisky, Stan. Only six weeks to go before next season, you know." He grinned and looked to Stan, fully expecting to be told where he might care to put his training.

"You can't leave free ale, Len. The whisky's free until ten o'clock. Either get it down now or store a few up for later."

Len smiled and moved sideways as Stan reached out to attract the attention of the waiter serving the group behind. His hands rested on the shoulder of a large portly gentleman, clad in a hand cut grey suit whose lapel was adorned with the largest of red roses in full bloom. He exuded an air of confidence and importance as others in his group listened to him rather than he to them. The neatness and precision of the knot in his tie above the regimental crest adorning it gave a hint as to his background and provided the perfect contrast to Stan's open neck and display of the beginnings of a hairy chest. A red handkerchief flopped carelessly, yet elegantly, from the top pocket of his suit, the sort of handkerchief that had never been designed to encounter so rude an object as a nose.

"Er, excuse me. Grab four whiskies off that tray please before the waiter goes," Stan implored in a slow but deliberate tone as if attempting to focus all his mind's attention on the delivery of each word. A smile creased the gentleman's face and, grasping four glasses between the fingers and thumbs of both hands, he offered them to Stan who by now had acquired his own tray for their safe keeping.

"Certainly Mr. Pearson," he replied, in an accent more suited to the verandah at the All England Croquet Club than the social room of the City Rugby League Club. Stan, who had not heard the name of Mr. Pearson used since his last visit to the Labour

Exchange four years ago, placed the drinks on his own tray and, after a mumbled "Thank you," proceeded to explain the need for four drinks. His new found friend listened politely and intently to the need to store up a whisky for the time when the free ale was finished at 10pm. With a nod he seemed reassured that he too could have one if he cared to look for the tray behind the rubber tree plant.

"Don't forget," Stan remarked as he attempted to focus his eyes upon the plant behind which he would place the tray of whisky. "Must be costing the sponsor a bloody packet for this lot." The gentleman nodded again and, turning to his small circle of friends added, "How interesting."

Ironically it was to be Mary's breasts which saved Stan Pearson from alcoholic disaster during the ensuing hour of celebration for, on a recommendation from Mac to view, he made frequent trips to the buffet table. Attacking a mound of pies nearest to Mary's serving position his eyes drank in the teasing delights whilst his stomach welcomed the pies as an antidote to the alcoholic content. Secure in the knowledge that the last remains of his free whisky nestled behind the large rubber tree plant in the corner of the room Stan savoured this interval with an earnest, if somewhat slurred conversation with Mac and Len as to the relative merits of the club's forwards for the next season - a discussion which prompted Mac to test Len over the possibility of a free transfer at the start of next season.

Having completed his benefit testimonial season Mac, now at the end of his playing career, would be seeking a free transfer to a lesser second division club where he might continue to play for another eighteen months. The playing held little relish for Mac whose knees, internally now resembled a scrap yard, but the prospect of a fat signing on fee for himself did interest him. Len,

"Look who it is. It's your mate Stan."

reaching for a further ham sandwich parried the question with, "You've got two years in you yet at City, Mac. We don't want to lose you yet."

Though Len well knew that if the intended rugby union signing came off in the close season then Mac could have his wish. Mac, about to develop an argument as to the urgency for a free transfer, was silenced by Len's arm lightly tapping him at the elbow and by the words,

"Ssh Mac, ssh. Mr Baker's about to speak. Besides you'll never leave City. We'll have to pay the R.S.P.C.A. to have you put down at the back of the stand."

To cries of "Order, Order. Let's have some hush," from the back of the social room Harry Baker, the club chairman, mounted the small stage, stubbed his cigarette into a small ashtray which lay on top of the piano and placed his glass of gin alongside. Harry, as befits a successful chairman of the Wembley winners, had rarely stopped smiling since the cup had been lifted at the stadium but his face displayed a wrinkle or two as he grappled with the complexities of the microphone now thrust into his hand.

"One, two, one, two," babbled across the room when he found the correct switch and untangled his feet from the yards of flex which lay around the stage and passed beneath the tables alongside. Harry achieved the necessary 'Hush' and, after adding his congratulations to the players and his thanks to the club staff for their endeavours at the weekend, he indicated his main task of the evening. He warmed to his task of introducing to the assembled guests the new president to be of City Rugby League Club - Sir George Gardiner of Bravo Breweries, the sponsors of the evening buffet party. All eyes turned to the corner of the small stage, hands clapped automatically as the portly gentleman in the grey suit mounted the steps - the self same gentleman whom Len had invited to be his guest at drinks, not half an hour before. Shaking hands with Mr. Baker he surveyed the room intently, keeping the microphone in his right hand at the side of his leg. Silence. He peered through the rising cigarette smoke to the back of the room until he recognised what he was searching for.

Stan's eyes knew what he was searching for as his gaze met that of Sir George. Stan gulped on his whisky, swallowing the ice cube whole. Len Topping pressed him on the foot with his own shoe as if to draw his attention to the stage. No need, Mac whispered, "Look who it is. It's your mate, Stan."

"Bloody 'ell," whispered Stan, through his teeth from behind the whisky glass with which he attempted to cover up his mouth. "How the hell did I know. Never seen him before."

Sir George Gardiner, sure of his find, raised his microphone, switched on the sound and leaned forward to address the guests. In his cultivated accent, obviously well practised on many a minion at the Croquet Club he directed his gaze in Stan's direction and, allowing his face the slightest of smiles said, "Before I add my congratulations to the team I wonder if Mr Pearson would mind passing me my whisky from behind that rubber tree plant?"

"Mr. Armstrong?"

"Cup of tea, Mr. Armstrong?"

"Oh yes, Jean. I'd love one. I wondered where you'd got to. Watch your head on that hatch. It needs fixing. It keeps slipping down."

"I've been taking the French francs back to the bank for Mr. Baker. He took far too much currency for that trip. He's lost about three pounds changing it back to sterling. And I've paid Gregsons for the coach to the airport out of the money I got back."

"Good Jean, that saves me a trip. I'd like a cup of tea, love."

"Won't be a minute, Mr. Armstrong."

Good girl that, dedicated to the job. She saved me a trip with that coach bill. 'End of season celebration trip,' Ben Higson said. If it had been at the beginning of the season we would have won nothing....

"Entente Cordiale"

The sight of Sid lying on his back, slumped along the bench in the Marseille airport transit lounge, his arm hanging limply to the floor, was hardly in keeping with 'our image abroad' which the City chairman had desired prior to the trip. The friendly match between the Catalan XIII of France and City had been intended to promote good relations and to provide the City players with an enjoyable weekend after their exertions at Wembley the previous week. For both Sid and Len Topping however, the week had proved to be an unnerving one.

Only on the morning of the team's departure for France had Len Topping's nerves calmed and a sense of quiet satisfaction settled upon him, an emotion far removed from his experiences sat on the trainers bench at Wembley the previous Saturday. Like the players, Len too needed a rest and what better than an end of season outing to France to soothe the nerves and relieve the tension of that hectic eighty minutes spent in the magnificent stadium.

Only Len could explain his strained condition whilst watching City's backs probe for the decisive opening in the second half of the Challenge Cup Final. Forty minutes of hell and torture for Len, sitting alongside the touchline and unable to play any active role. The forward probes of Harrison and Todd had gone close but, midway through the half, he had known that with the score at seven points to six points in Warrington's favour the result was in the balance. The next try would take the game. He had been well aware that only a supreme effort or an extraordinary piece of luck would take City and Len to victory. Now in France, was the time for relaxation or so he had thought.

Sid too had had thoughts of relaxing after that hectic Cup Final week spent loading and unloading kit out of an array of deluxe motor coaches. But, like Len, he didn't bargain for the unexpected which often occurs on all rugby trips abroad.

Sid's downfall had begun on the Sunday morning at the reception prior to the match against the Catalan XIII. He had attempted to follow faithfully the instructions given to him by Len who saw himself as coach supreme - "too clever for these frogs". The reception had been held in Le Restaurant Sporting which nestled in a narrow cobbled alleyway close to the ground. Len had given strict instructions that his team were only to drink orange squash before the game and he was delighted to see the French opposition arrive, clad in their red and blue tracksuits, all eager to hear the welcoming speeches. Sid seemed to find the opening speech, delivered by the owner of the restaurant and the club president, to be a most absorbing one. Though he faced in the direction of the club's president, Sid's eyes and mind were concentrated on the vast array of bottles resting on the trestle table behind the speaker. The effect of so many bottles of champagne on Sid seemed to cause each eye to gain an independent suspension as he surveyed the number and made a quick count of the guests.

"There's at least two bottles each," mused Sid.

The number also had not been lost on Len who, nodding his agreement at what seemed the relevant places in the speeches, nudged Sid in the back in an effort to attract his attention.

"Get among those French players, Sid. Make sure they sup all that ale. They'll never run around the field in the second half. I'll keep ours off it."

The chance to serve City in such a capacity came to few men and Sid, not being one to miss such an opportunity to serve his club and his own interests, determined to do his best. At the conclusion of the speeches, and armed with a champagne bottle under each arm, Sid endeavoured to mingle with the opposition. Exchanging nods and toasts he proceeded to make use of his linguistic talents.

"Bon ale, this, monsieur, eh?"

Such choice expressions flowed freely from the tongue, especially when the champagne began to take its hold. Sensing that the French players seemed oblivious to the match and noting the vast quantities of alcohol they were drinking, Len allowed his lads a sip for 'entente cordiale' sake. Meanwhile Sid, now revelling in his undercover work for City, chattered more excitedly as a never ending supply of glasses were raised to his lips. His gloating however came to a sorry end. On learning from a naive student translator that only the Catalan second team had attended the function he was stopped in mid slurp. Staring incredulously at the translator he carefully fingered the stem of his glass, tried to focus his eyes on it, then, on turning to his mentor, was heard to whisper,

"Len, we've been bloody done!"

Without waiting for a reply he made a dramatic slump to the floor. Sid had indeed been 'done'. Whilst the Catalan first team limbered up at the stadium Sid had entertained their second team squad in such regal fashion that the next twenty four hours, and especially the last hour awaiting the aeroplane's departure, were only a blur to him. Now lying on the bench in the Marseille transit lounge, he was totally unconcerned at the club's loss of a match which had proved to be a dour affair, governed by a referee who had seemed to be France's answer to Charlie Chaplin. Sid was, however, very concerned at the loss of the team's entire supply of jockstraps which, in his alcoholic haze following the match, he had mislaid. The thought of twenty assorted-size jockstraps loose on the Black market in the port of Marseille was enough to put fear into any man. The fear of facing 'Arry on his return, minus twenty jockstraps, was too much for Sid. Rising painfully from the bench he attempted to relieve all thoughts of their future meeting whilst at the same time reducing his headache. Opening a bottle of light ale he squashed two Alka Seltzers inside the neck and having produced a steady fizz from out of the bottle, commented to Len, sat wearily alongside him. "You can't trust the water on the continent, Len."

"You can't trust anybody here," replied Len, grateful to hear the call over the tannoy for the waiting aircraft on the tarmac outside, and reflecting ruefully on the antics of the local referee. City's loss had been a sore point with Len, and, scouring the transit lounge for anything which the players and directors had left behind, he was thankful that the weekend was nearing its close. He propelled Sid, now clearing himself of the froth of the bottle, through the swing doors where he left him in the guidance of 'Con' Chapman. Relieved of Sid, if only temporarily, he looked behind to see a small carpet, rolled and tied with a piece of string, leaning against a pillar which had previously blocked his vision. "Strange, somebody leaving a carpet behind," he thought. "Still, it must be somebody's on the flight. I'd better take it through the gate." Strolling over to pick up the small carpet he whistled softly to himself the last strains of the Marseillaise, having been unable to get the tune out of his head since the formalities of the anthems before the game. Meanwhile the players, along with the rest of the passengers bound for Manchester, had congregated around the passport check desk alongside the glass swing doors, all by now eager to be on their way home. The players, still basking in the glory of their Cup Final win and already forgetful of their defeat in France, mingled happily with the other passengers. A few signing autographs and others, notably Mac, engaging a pretty young brunette in earnest conversation, noticeably not about the arts of front row play. Her mother, a short tubby woman, looked around in alarmed fashion as if appealing for help to extricate her daughter from the attentions of Mac. No help, if any was needed, was forthcoming. The daughter would be left to sidestep Mac herself. Len approached the stragglers at the back and, carrying the roll of carpet under his arm, waited quietly at the rear where he began to re-read the headlines of Friday's edition of the Daily Mail which lay on the top of a passenger's travel bag.

"Hijackers strike again. Bomb secretly placed aboard plane."
Len looked at the paper. He looked at the carpet beneath his arm. He looked back at the newspaper and suddenly he didn't like the thought of what he was doing.

"Suppose somebody has planted a bomb in the carpet? Why was it lying there?"

As the crowd slowly formed into the semblance of a queue he found himself being edged nearer to the passport desk with his mind unable to satisfy himself over what he thought to be childish ideas in his head. He looked behind to check whether anyone was watching his movements. A tall, dark-skinned customs officer, proud of his new uniform, stood seemingly unaware, rolling a cigarette in the palm of his hand.

"Never know when they're watching you. I must be bloody mad," thought Len, but he felt himself at a loss to explain his holding of the carpet if there happened to be a bomb inside.

"Must get rid of it."

Walking to the front of the queue, seemingly to help Sid to find his passport, he carefully yet casually placed the carpet onto the floor next to the metal barrier. The customs officer only took his eyes momentarily off the rolled cigarette to glance at him before placing it inside a small black tin box perched on the sill of the window against which he was leaning. Had he noticed? His stance was too casual for Len's liking. Customs officers, even French ones, didn't roll cigarettes on duty, thought Len. He considered the whole affair to be a figment of his vivid imagination yet, on seeing Sid through the barrier and onto the aeroplane, he quickly made his way to the toilet before taking up his reserved seat at the rear of the plane.

"Get a grip on yourself, Len," he thought as he smiled into the toilet mirror, "whoever heard of a bloody bomb in a carpet. Still, it's off my hands now."

He straightened his red tie, smoothed his hands down the front and across the crest of City R.L.F.C. mopped his brow with a paper towel and then returned to his seat at the back of the aeroplane. Easing himself into the cushioned seat Len adjusted his legs into a comfortable position, glanced at the emergency instructions clipped to the back of the seat in front of him and then closed his eyes. Peace. The prospect of a couple of hours sleep during the flight home became more appealing to him once the rigours of the take off were over but, before he could settle, he was shaken by a firm grip from behind. Mac leaned forward, relaxed his grip on Len's arm and said,

"I put your carpet on the empty seat across the aisle. You left it at the barrier when you were helping Sid with his passport. Thought you were supposed to attend to the players. You can't look after yourself, Len, never mind us," quipped Mac and leaned back in his seat to place a set of earphones on his head.

After a period of silent cursing Len spent the next hour with the corner of his right eye transfixed on the carpet which reclined on the seat behind him across the aisle.

"If no one on board has claimed it, then it must have been planted on me. It can't be a bomb, the stewardess'll think I'm bloody nuts." Len's mind exploded with thoughts for an hour until, convinced that if it were to be a bomb, then there must be a ticking from a time mechanism, he determined to reassure himself. Sliding down into the seat he leaned over the arm rest until his head was almost level with the rest and, protruding into the aisle, he stretched his neck and head across. He strained to hear any telling sound coming from inside the carpet. He leaned further out into the aisle and sank even lower into his seat when the stern eye of the stewardess glared at him. In the act of leaning over her trolley in order to serve coffee to the passengers she had misinterpreted Len's contortions as a vain attempt on his part to study her legs, smugly fitting into a pale green skirt. With her contemptuous eye she pinned him back to the seat as a butterfly specimen and forced him to close his eyes, feigning sleep, in a feeble attempt to avoid her glare.

Was a ticking noise in his head coming from the carpet or was it coming from the new watch he had purchased in the Duty Free shop at Manchester? No, it couldn't be. Quartz watches don't tick. Or at least they shouldn't do. Neither coffee, sleep, nor conversation could shake the thoughts from Len's mind as the next hour stretched out slowly before the plane's eventual landing. The successful landing however seemed to galvanise Len into action for, springing from his seat, he seized the carpet, placed it under his right arm and strode forward to be first at the rear exit door. Waiting impatiently, but somewhat embarrassed to face the same shapely stewardess who had transfixed him with her gaze, he looked through the cabin windows to catch sight of the steps being wheeled alongside the door. The wheel lock of the

"There in bold lettering imprinted in the centre of the carpet lay its message 'Marseille Transit Lounge'."

cabin door was turned, a red light above went out, and the door swung open to reveal the murky grey of a damp Manchester skyline. Len was bounding down the steps two at a time, long before the stewardess, in the act of donning her cap, could issue any goodbyes, however forced. His feet were on the ground. He heaved a sigh of relief, strode away from the steps and, carefully avoiding a small patch of water lying on the runway, he placed the roll of carpet on the tarmac surface. He snapped the string which was neatly tied around the centre of the carpet.

"I must know. Can't be anything there. They'll think I'm bloody daft. Still, must take a look now."

Such thoughts accumulated in his head as, like the Genie in the Christmas Aladdin production, he flicked the carpet away from himself with both hands yet maintained his grip at one end. Laying the carpet open on the ground his face suddenly regained its colour when no fiendish mechanical contraption was to be seen. On casting his eyes over the red and blue carpet his jaw sagged, his eyes opened wider, and his shoulders dropped at the message which confronted him. There in bold lettering, imprinted in the centre of the carpet lay its message,

"Marseille Transit Lounge".

"Nice cup of tea, that, Jean."

"I'll leave the cups until I get back this afternoon, Mr Armstrong. John's picking me up for lunch. Oh, I forgot to tell you. Argosy Travel rang early this morning about Len Topping and his Australian visit."

"That's okay, Jean. I've spoken to them. I'll see you tomorrow."

A good deal from Argosy Travel. I must put their cheque in the post on my way home, and that's my lot for the season. I think we can afford to have these offices decorated in the summer. That white wall gives a bad impression with all the hand marks around the door. I shouldn't stick posters and fixture sheets on it with sellotape either. Always brings the paint off when they are taken down. I'll see Ben Higson about borrowing one of his apprentices for a couple of days when I get back from holidays. Now all I need is a stamp and Argosy Travel can have their £290 cheque. Wish I was out there with Warren and Stan, watching the Test instead of sitting in a deckchair at Llandudno with the little'un burying my feet in the sand. It'll probably be Stan Pearson ringing me on reverse charges from Sydney to tell me how they got on at Riverina. I'll find out tonight in the Evening News. It's far cheaper....

"Down Under"

"There's no way we should have lost that game today. Bloody robbed. Nobody'll ever believe you back home when you talk about referees. He gave them everything." Though seemingly talking to himself and the empty bed of Arthur Crossley alongside, Warren Bates addressed his observations in the direction of Stan Pearson who, stripped to his underpants, was beginning to shave at the small sink near his bed across the room. Warren, already in bed and reading the day's Test Match programme, looked up and surveyed the bare brown walls of the Olympic Hotel, Sydney, Australia, their monotony only punctuated by a large, brown, wardrobe alongside Stan's bed, obviously seized with loving care from some stock clearance sale. The draught coming under the balcony windows from the cold but clear night outside had caused Warren to pull the blanket to his chin whilst the two pairs of white shorts, recently washed and airing over the chair back, added to the general dampness of the room.

"Two tries to one yet we still lost. Goalkicks!"

A flick of his fingers caused the programme to fall to the floor at the side of his bed.

"Sick of reading that rubbish. You'd think the Aussies were supermen if you believed these programme notes."

The clanking of the pipes around the room rose to a crescendo as Stan emptied the contents of the sink, scuffed his hand around the basin, replaced the plug, and let in more hot water. Squirting a white blob onto the palm of his left hand he prepared to cover his face in shaving foam, carefully avoiding the movements of his mouth as he replied.

"You've got to dictate to the Aussies up front. We didn't have the pack to do it. Told Hudson he had picked the wrong men. Too many runners and not enough tacklers. You can't let an Aussie forward run or he will run all day. We should have thrown some stick out early on."

Warren leaned over the side of the bed to stretch and reach for the discarded programme in order to give further study to the composition of the Great Britain pack. Taylor, Speed, Davies, Collinson, Crossley, Raeburn - his eyes scanned the names in the pack as if for signs of confirmation of Stan's theory.

"There was something lacking today alright, Stan. It just wasn't there."

"Discipline and a professional attitude, that's what was lacking and has been for the past week...Townsville, Cairns, Rockhampton, they're only a bunch of amateurs. Those wins in Queensland went to their heads, too much sunshine and giant prawns for tea. We were lucky in that first Test at Lang Park. If they had had a goalkicker then they would have beaten us. Good job Carlisle was injured. Hudson got too cocky, didn't believe me when I told him to wait until we got to the Cricket ground here in Sydney. Since we've been here it's been like a holiday camp. Everybody has forgotten about the rugby."

Warren, rather naively, lay his programme aside again and looked intently at Stan who was looking back through the small mirror above the sink. He lifted his right ear lobe carefully and gently with his left hand and proceeded to apply firm strokes with his razor. The conversation stopped whilst Stan rinsed the razor in the hot water in the sink. Warren waited and reached again for the programme.

"I ask you, what about Thursday? Forty-eight hours before a Test Match. All down at the Cross! Hardly the right attitude for professionals," erupted Stan.

Warren made no answer but, on flicking through the pages, his eyes alighted on the very nature of Stan's indignation. Alongside the listing of the tour itinerary was the bold lettering of the advertisement offering the delights of the "Gas Light Rooms" - "Five floors of Discos" - "Your host Steve Berry".

Steve Berry had indeed been there at the Gas Light rooms on that particular Thursday, in fact he had never left the party since the arrival of the Great Britain tourists in Sydney. A thin, somewhat effeminate man in his dark grey mohair suit, he had somehow sprang up in the Olympic Hotel Lounge, at the training in Sydney, at the reception in the Eastern Suburbs club, in fact anywhere that the party were engaged. His night club had been placed at the disposal of the touring party, no doubt in return for the good match seats which he had gained for the Second Test and for the publicity which the Gas Light Rooms had commanded in the daily press. Warren's face broke into a huge grin as his mind recollected that Thursday night when two dozen of the players had been Steve Berry's guests at his exclusive fifth floor special-members disco, all huddled around the three tables which had been placed together for their welcome. The most endearing welcome to the club was in fact given by the many hostesses and assorted Australian beauties who gathered around to bask in the reflected glory of the sporting heroes, all hoping for a feature in the press next morning. Many of the players however, as they peered at the variety of female shapes beneath the dim red lighting, were hoping for much more, none more so than man's answer to King Kong, Tony Darley, the Hunslet prop, and his sidekick on the tour Alf Collinson the second row from Swinton. Tony was a seasoned campaigner of some twelve seasons in the game to whom selection for the tour had come as a huge shock to

*"Two blondes of similar proportions
had attracted their attention."*

the Rugby League world and to himself in particular. Now at the latter end of his career he had already joined that section of the party whose lot is to play in the minor matches and keep the flag flying in the outback areas - a group of players unkindly referred to as the 'Ham and Eggers'. Nevertheless, along with Alf Collinson he had developed as the wag of the tour party, not only for his humorous comment but on account of his slowness of thought and his typical prop's face. A man of huge proportions, some seventeen stones and six feet four inches, his face looked as if it had been moulded by some blind Italian sculptor working in second hand marble. On a face knotted and gnarled with bumps and scar tissue, his nose had obviously been rushed before the Italian's tea break. A huge blob of skin and broken bone, distorted in varying places, had obviously been thrown to the centre of the face and left to dry for a day or two with disastrous results. Two large cauliflower ears lay either side of his head, one seemingly higher than the other, a sight which prompted the remark from Alf Collinson, that, "When he rang the Hunslet Lonely Hearts club they rang back and told him they weren't that bloody lonely."

Two blondes of similar proportions had attracted their attention and, despite a degree of ribbing that both had surely played league for Australia at some time, both players had spent a couple of hours plying the girls with drinks and whispering 'sweet nothings' in their ears. Steve Berry hovered in the background obviously delighted in his new found friends from Great Britain and attended to their every request for drinks but, along with Warren in whom he had confided, he took intense pleasure at the chatting of the foursome in the corner.

"You'd have to pay to watch matings like this in the Ape House at the zoo," commented Wilf Raeburn to Steve.

"Hope they don't mate," chuckled Steve as he offered a knowing wink in Warren's direction.

Unaware of the interest which this romantic collusion had caused, Tony Darley rose from his seat and pulled the seat back from under his lady friend as she too rose to stand. He turned to Warren and with a huge grin spread across his face to reveal a sparkling set of white teeth, all false, and with his eye winking rapidly he advised,

"Tell Billy not to come back to the hotel room before two o'clock. We've some business to attend to, me and Alf."

Unfortunately or fortunately as it turned out their two ladies had some business to attend to before leaving and excused themselves to visit the GENTS.

"They've gone to the GENTS. Did you see that? Quick, tell them they're in the wrong place," panicked Alf.

"Eh," was Tony's studied reaction.

"I'm not having those two in the other place," laughed the proprietor Steve Berry.

"I'd have a riot on my hands from the women."

A realisation of the implications slowly dawned in Tony's head as he grappled with the realities of their instant courtship. Alf Collinson stood open mouthed down the corridor,

"You mean they're, they're....."

"I do," replied Steve, before Alf could complete his amazed utterance. Tony, who had been 'eating' his 'mates' ear lobes as a romantic overture throughout the night suddenly felt sick and leaned heavily upon the table as his team mates roared with laughter at the revelations.

"You mean....."

"Never mind that. Let's bugger off before they come out. What are we going to do? Come on. I'm off. Oh Hell!" roared Alf who, along with Tony, beat a hasty retreat from the Disco with roars of delight from the players ringing in his ears.

A hectic start to the night and one which, despite the smile upon Warren's face as he lay in bed, had also provided smiles at his expense too.

"I must be the only normal player on this trip," quipped Stan. "My mother always said I shouldn't mix with rugby league players. She said they would lead me astray. She never mentioned ex Union players though. She thought they were all clean and healthy."

Warren's smile grew larger not only at the thought of the incident to which Stan was referring but at the sight of Stan, in his underpants, with one foot in the sink.

"I'll have a bath after the match tomorrow," had been the preliminary to his Stork like act of balancing on one leg whilst rinsing the foot of the other in a sink which was too small and too highly placed on the wall.

"I've heard of simple Welshmen in the hills but never one who couldn't spot a 'queer' a mile off. You've got me worried about rooming with you Batesy. Thank God Arthur's in here too. It's been a bloody circus since last Saturday, Rugby has been second best to everything for some of the lads. Too many think it's one long holiday out here."

Stan, by now steady on both feet, replaced his shaving gear in the toilet bag and, having given his feet a last drying rub with the towel draped across his bed, made for the room door, clad only in his underpants, to seek the toilet along the corridor. Warren turned onto his back and, tucking up the double pillows beneath his head, placed his hands also beneath as he reflected on Stan's damning comment, "Nobody's mind has been on the rugby."

No one could accuse Warren Bates of not having his mind on the

rugby for he had thought of little else since he had caught sight
of the placards advertising the Manchester Evening News for that
April 20th edition - "Bates makes Tour as utility back". Within
half a season he had stepped from the small village of Crynant
outside Neath, to Sydney via City R.L.F.C. with flight stops at
Geneva, Calcutta, and Hong Kong. Spurred on by a casual but
indiscreet comment on the plane from Tom Hudson, the Great
Britain coach, who had expressed his doubts as to the wisdom of
Warren's selection, he had determined since rising that morning
to give of his best. Though Warren had built himself up mentally
for the match few players could have escaped the excitement and
tension which had built up during the morning. Standing on
their balcony which overlooked the pedestrian crossing at the
corner of the road and the famed cricket ground, both Warren
and Stan could not fail to appreciate the importance of the
occasion as they surveyed the ground filling up with spectators to
watch the junior matches. The Australians below their balcony
surged across the road carrying large cooler boxes in assorted
colours and filled with vast amounts of canned beer with which to
quench their thirst as they awaited the clash of the main
contestants, Great Britain v Australia. Others, mainly younger
ones in open neck shirts, called into the public bar downstairs to
fight their way amongst the throbbing mass inside to order their
Midis or Schooners before continuing on their way. Warren and
Stan too had joined this throng of eager spectators as, along with
the rest of the Great Britain side, they made their way along the
short road past the Showground to the players' entrance at the
Cricket Ground. The banter and the good humoured comments
of, "You're done today, you Pommie bastards," was sufficient to
add that extra mental edge to Warren's state of mind prior to
such an important game. They had left the glare of the sunlight

on entering the bowels of the huge stadium, past the long bar, and up the stairs to their dressing room overlooking the pitch, and the steps which led on to the playing area.

The sound of Stan's footsteps returning along the corridor from his visit to the toilet sharply focussed Warren's thought in his head as all manner of sights and memories flooded in of his eventful day. The Union Jacks, flying high above the dense crowd, his two tries, the six penalty goals of the aboriginal fullback 'Chip' Carlisle, "bloody bent referee", fifty-five thousand hostile Australians screaming for more points. Stan entered and, opening the door of the large cupboard along the wall, complained to himself,

"Fancy getting up at six o'clock for a blasted match. Who the hell ever fixed up a match at Riverina the day after a Test wants his head seeing to. It'll be fifty nil when we get there. Showing the flag. Those who voted this through in Leeds want to be here now. Where's my pyjamas?"

He reached inside the cupboard and retrieved a pair of pyjamas as yet unused from beneath a pile of jerseys and shorts.

"Look at these. Far too big. I told Doreen to take them back to Marks and Spencer before I came out. I could fit you and Arthur in these pants. She'll have to take them back when I get home."

Warren nodded to both his assertions for he certainly had had his fill of the Aussies who, proud of their victory, had been eager to drum the ears of the British party all that night at THE PINK PARROT CLUB where they had gone supposedly to escape their failure of the afternoon. Warren and Stan had quietly left during the striptease cabaret, while a husky dancer was gyrating on the floor to the accompanying sounds of 'My Boomerang Won't Come Back'. Neither Stan nor Warren had cared what she did with her boomerang or whether she would ever get it back, as they sought the sanctuary of their beds.

"The things I do for my country. Hope I'm remembered in the Honours List next year," quipped Stan. "Throw that programme away, I'm putting out the light. Reading about them won't beat them."

"I think you're right Stan," replied Warren, as he turned onto his side to await the dark.

"Can't wait for the Third Test though. Bet Hudson's sick about me winning the man of the match award."

Not as sick as me having to go to Riverina in the morning," replied Stan. "Hope Arthur gives us a knock at six o'clock."

"Right, I'll ask Doreen to give any letters to Len Topping and he can bring them out for you before the Third Test. No, no problem. I'm passing your house on my way home now. Yes, I'll tell her you beat Riverina by thirty-eight points to six. And you scored two tries. I'll not forget, Stan. Have a good Third Test, you and Warren."

He must have put the phone down. The line's gone dead. It's amazing that he's twelve thousand miles away, I could hear him as if he were in Fern Street. It's cost the club twenty quid though, you can bet. I shouldn't have turned back. I had a feeling it was Stan ringing before he goes to bed in Sydney. Never mind, Doreen will be pleased to hear from me. They're just like kids really, big, daft, kids. The trouble is it's usually me who has to wipe their noses and clean up their mess. I can lock this office door but it's difficult to put the game at one side. It's been a marvellous season. Hard work, bloody hard! But worth it. The pitch looks good, a nice coating of grass coming on the top now. All we need now is one of those electronic scoreboards that Wigan have. Heinz Beans sponsored theirs. I wonder would Hardman's Central Heating stretch their finances to that. I could put a radiator inside to keep the operator warm in winter! Not to worry. It'll soon be September again and we're off. The trouble with rugby league is that no matter how disillusioned you are, no matter how weary, the spirit perks up when 'T' Cup comes round again.

A pity Tony won't be with us next season. He did well for us in this season's cup run. A move to Swinton will be good for him and it's good for City - a few young faces around the changing rooms should add to the excitement when we have to defend the trophy....

"The Backhander"

The steady tap of his fingers on the top of the walnut table and the casual way in which he rolled his left hand around the whisky glass in front of him was a sure indication of a smug, contented Benjamin Higson. The others, at the close of the meeting, had left their seats and had grouped around the drinks cabinet where 'Con' Chapman who, daringly for him in the heat of a July evening, had removed his black pin stripe jacket, and dispensed drinks to Ted Partridge, Colin Taylor and Charles Cartwright. Ben remained seated in the chair at the head of the table, usually reserved for Chairman Harry Baker but who was at that moment on a month's holiday cruise in the West Indies, accompanied by his daughter and son in law. Ben remained for a few more lingering moments, his eyes focussed on the gold arm bands which raised Con's shirt sleeves above the wrist, but reflecting with quiet satisfaction upon the deal which he had successfully imposed upon the board. A deal which he had quietly manoeuvred through in the fortuitous absence of Harry. An absence which allowed Ben to sit as acting chairman and in which capacity he felt that he must justify his position and especially his ego by concluding such deals. With the last drum of the fingers and a quick gulp at the remaining contents of the glass he pushed his seat back and rose from the table with the slow deliberation one expects from a Prime Minister at the conclusion of a crucial War Cabinet. He had satisfied his own ego, he now needed it to be flattered.

"Fill me up, 'Con', with another," he said in a low, hushed, voice and then, with considerable relish and in much stronger tones, he observed, "We'll not regret it. You must be firm when you have to take decisions. We can't let sympathy get in the way of running a club like City." Ben placed his glass onto the drop leaf of the drinks cabinet and placed his arm on Con's shoulder as he was about to pour a large whisky for Colin Taylor, standing at his side. "I'll be back in fifteen minutes. I told Smith I would like a word with him after training. It won't take me long. He'll be coming up to the lounge from training by now. Carry on without me for a while."

Colin Taylor looked up from his drink as Ben crossed the floor and out through the door, knowing well that there was little else of consequence to discuss for the remainder of the weekly Board meeting and that if there was, then Ben certainly would not have left them to themselves. Colin knew he had been beaten in the discussions which had centred around Tony Smith but he only hoped that Ben would continue to have things all his own way with Tony, if only for the good of the club. Yet somehow he felt content to leave the conclusions to Ben for, knowing the player as he did, he chuckled inwardly in the knowledge that Tony would put up a good fight in a clinch with Benjamin Higson.

The clinch between Ben and the board in regard to the possible transfer of Tony Smith to Swinton had been no contest, for Ben, having selected the contestants, time, date, and the venue of the fight, had easily emerged as the winner on a technical knockout. The only adversary worthy of Ben's attentions was safely out of the room, lying on the top deck of his cruise ship dreaming of the season to come. With the added bonus of Sam Cartwright's absence, owing to a heavy bout of flu which had necessitated his staying indoors, Ben had only needed to muster 'Con' and Ted Partridge to the table to ensure his desires, no matter how Colin or Charles Cartwright viewed the transfer. Despite Charles' plea for retaining Tony as cover for Mac's impending departure he

had displayed little fight against Ben's wishes, only joining the fray
as proof of his loyalty to his captain at sea whom he felt sure
would have opposed Ben on the intended sale. Colin Taylor, as
ever playing the role of the players' plaintiff and sure in the
knowledge that he would be defeated, had argued strongly,
though not too strongly to ruffle the proceedings, that Tony be
kept on City's books. Ben's tactics and cold logic had carried the
vote despite his precise summing up at the end. "The position is
that Swinton have made an approach for Tony Smith and are
willing to go to £10,000 for him as part of their build up to
getting back into Division One next season. They've bought a few
junior league players, a couple of Union converts and now feel
that Tony is just the prop to give them the necessary lead and
experience up front for the next two seasons. We have Tony
Smith, now aged 33 and suffering from a bad back. He finished
off the season in style in the Premiership Trophy and in the win at
Wembley. We can get that money for him now, in twelve months
time we'll get nothing for him and he'll be on the scrap heap.
It's a good move for us and I am sure I can make Smith see that it
is a good move for him. £500 will see him right you'll see."
On leaving the Board Room Mr. Higson had approached the
Cabaret Lounge with the assured air of one who knows he is
going to get his own way. He felt that he had all the cards to do
the deal but, within five minutes of Tony's arrival, he soon
realised that, although Tony had no cards in his hands, he had
placed a few jokers up his sleeve, ready for any bidding.
Unbeknown to Ben, Tony also knew well of the suggested transfer
by means of a discreet phone call from the Swinton coach who,
eager to gain his signature on any registration forms, had also
informed him of the suggested fee. Tony too realised that the
move would be good for him and would require little persuasion

from Ben as to its conclusion. But, it would take £1,000 to tempt him away from what he knew to be a not too optimistic future. Having left training early to arrive in the lounge a few minutes before Ben, he had reflected on the alternatives, alone at the bar, save the steward cleaning a few glasses behind and the young girl placing drip mats on the lines of red plastic topped tables.

Only he knew how much trouble he was having from his back, only he heard the curses which issued forth after that York game as he lay for hours at night seeking a comfortable position on the mattress. He knew he would never see a testimonial benefit for ten years service at City, but with two more seasons in the Second Division he could pick up a lot of money for less intense rugby. Yes, Ben Higson would have little trouble persuading him of the attractions on the playing side but he would have to do much talking on 'the backhander'.

Tony had listened patiently to Ben explaining the intricacies of the suggested transfer, his attention only interrupted by the pint of mild which he offered to his lips and which at every gulp seemed to bring greater beads of sweat rising from his forehead, the results of a hard training session.

"So that's it. It's good for City, good for Swinton, but especially is it good for you," concluded Ben.

Tony felt cynically relieved at this show of concern for his welfare, most unbecoming of the club's Vice Chairman, and parried any reply by ordering drinks from the bar for both of them.

"A pint of mild and a whisky for Mr. Higson, Harold, before the rush gets in," he urged as he noticed Tom Harvey enter from the Lottery Office door behind the half-moon stage at the far end of the concert room.

"And a Bitter," shouted Tom as he approached, in sideways fashion, trying to negotiate the narrow passages down the long lines of tables. Higson's composure was beginning to slip as he had already realised that he was playing with Tony on away ground amongst his own spectators. He knew he should never have left the Board Room but instead have invited Tony to play with him on his own pitch. The intervention of hooker Tom Harvey at this delicate stage was more than he had bargained for. "Warren's had a good match in the Second Test, I see, Mr. Higson. He got the Man of the Match. Didn't give much of a report on Stan in the papers I read. The Third Test should be a blinder, I think we can win it if we get a fair crack from the ref." "Yes, Tom, but I don't think our side is good enough. We've not forwards to match their speed and size. And we could have done with a good hooker, eh?" he observed as he gave Tom a friendly dig in the ribs.

"Aye, we'd have given 'em some stick eh, Tony," laughed Tom, before placing the pint glass of Bitter to his lips. Tony, in the act of counting his change on the bar top, smiled whilst Ben fingered the stem of his whisky glass deep in thought as to how he might remove Tom from the company. He need not have bothered for Tom was too good a professional not to sense that a meeting between a 33 year old prop and the club's acting Chairman, after training, alone at the Lounge Bar, was hardly designed for planning their holidays. His realisation, coupled with a wink and a movement away of Tony's head, was sufficient to send him scurrying to join a group of players making their way to the other corner of the bar, all careful to keep their distance from Tony and Mr. Higson.

Ben, self conscious and somewhat embarrassed, looked along the full length of the bar, uninterrupted, to the cluster of players at the far corner and realised what it was like to be a human book end. "Well, what do you think, Tony? It's a great chance for you to add

"I'll need a £1,000 out of it"

to an illustrious career. You can do a lot of good for Swinton," resumed Ben, now giving his full attention to settle the matter quickly after Harvey's untimely interruption. "I must give them an answer tonight."

"It's me who'll give the answers and it depends on how much good it does for me, not Swinton," replied Tony.

He paused to drink from his glass but more to review his tactics with Ben.

He knew a long protracted bargaining would merely see him worn down by Ben's evasive answers and suggestions. He had the jokers, he knew that whatever cards Ben held he was essentially a hard headed businessman. He must throw his jokers in at the opening and gamble on the whole deal.

"I'll need £1,000 out of it, Ben."

Higson remained motionless, save the movement of a finger up the stem of his glass. "I'm 33, my back's knackered, I'll not last the season out. I'll have to retire," Tony snapped coldly and bluntly, "and I want £1,000 if there's to be ten thousand for you." Ben's fingers tightened on the stem, only the slight puckering of his lips and movement of his cheekbones indicated an inner wince at the figure suggested by Tony. He knew he might have to go to a thousand but little did he know that at the playing of his only hand he would be naked at the table, and not at his table either.

"Ten thousand's only a figure been suggested," replied Ben, stalling for time. "Ben, I know all the facts," stressed Tony now arriving for the kill and about to lay his final trump, "I've done well out of the game and at 32 I'm not bothered about retiring now. If Swinton knew about my back you wouldn't get ten pence, never mind ten thousand. And if I stay, in 12 months you know I'll be finished. It's simple. I go to Swinton, you get £9,000 I get

£1,000. I stay or retire, you get nothing. I'm happy to do as you wish, Ben."

"You wouldn't retire Tony."

"Try me Ben." Ben knew he dare not. Swinton were awaiting a call at ten o'clock and he knew full well that if the answer was no they would look elsewhere. Ben knew that Tony Smith could spite his face if he wished, but he knew that even £9,000 for a 32 year old with a bad back and with 12 months left in the game would buy four juniors.

"One thousand Ben?" Ben grinned wide for the first time.

"Do you want another drink, Tony?"

"One thousand," Tony replied and nodded slowly, his own face breaking into a grin in response to Ben's.

"We're going to the Black Horse for a last one. Are you coming Tony?" a cry came from the other end of the bar in the shape of Tom Harvey. "Is he joining the Board Mr. Higson? He's no money you know," joked Tom. Ben turned away from Tony to smile at Tom and his remarks. Tony raised his pint aloft behind, to reply, "Be with you in a minute. We're just discussing something to our mutual benefit!"

Also by Ray French

My Kind of Rugby

More Kind of Rugby

Coaching Rugby League

Rugby League Lions

Ray French's 100 Great Rugby League Players

The Match of My Life

Running Rugby